GENERAL ALARM

ALSO BY CHARLES F. HAYWOOD

Minutemen and Mariners
Yankee Dictionary
Eastward the Sea
You Need a Complete Rest
No Ship May Sail

GENERAL ALARM

A Dramatic Account of Fires and Fire-fighting in America

CHARLES F. HAYWOOD

Illustrated

Dodd, Mead & Company · New York

Copyright © 1967 by Charles F. Haywood
All rights reserved
No part of this book may be reproduced in any form
without permission in writing from the publisher
Library of Congress Catalog Card Number: 67-12711

Printed in the United States of America
by The Haddon Craftsmen, Inc., Scranton, Penna.

Library
I.U.P.
Indiana, Pa.

628.92 H336g
c.1

THIS BOOK IS DEDICATED TO THE OFFICERS AND MEN OF THE

Fire Department of Lynn, Massachusetts

WHO BY THEIR COURAGE AND DEVOTION TO THE DUTY OF PROTECTING THEIR CITY TYPIFY THE AMERICAN FIREMEN.

Acknowledgments

I WISH TO ACKNOWLEDGE the assistance I have received from the Lynn Public Library, the Salem Public Library, the Detroit Public Library, the Lynn Historical Society and, above all, the National Fire Protection Association of Boston and its vast store of facts and knowledge in the field of fire prevention and fire fighting.

The help given me by Roscoe W. Hilliker, Roger Maguire, and District Chief Joseph E. Scanlon, Jr., all of Lynn, Harold S. Walker of Marblehead, and Deputy Chief William P. Lindecker of San Francisco is deeply appreciated. Particularly do I wish to mention what I gained from the knowledge, experience, and companionship of the late Alton Hall Blackington, known to all in Greater Boston and in New England as the greatest spark of them all. To know "Blackie" was an adventure in many fields, as well as a great experience in the warmth of human friendship.

Especially do I wish to express appreciation for the help given me by my wife, Dorothy C. Haywood, Chief Librarian of the Lynn Public Library. Assisting at first because it was a project of mine, she has become more and more interested, and at some not distant time she may rightfully be said to be one of that great fraternity known as sparks or buffs.

Preface

THIS BOOK tells the stories of many great battles with fire, battles which if lost meant a city in ruins. Some of these battles were lost and a path of devastation lay across a city, a path ending only at a lake or river or open country or at the ocean. Yet even on these days of disaster, when it seemed as if the element Fire had taken charge everywhere, there were moments of victory, places on the fire front where brave and determined men, fighting with everything they had, managed to check the advancing destruction.

Victory may be at a small point, such as the house of the valiant man who fought it out with the Great Chicago Fire and won and saved his home. Or victory may be on a broad front, as at the great battles at Jones Falls in Baltimore and at the Merchants Exchange in Boston. The Chicagoan fought with a bucket and mud and wet blankets and water from his own well. In Baltimore and in Boston forty or more steam fire engines, every one of them working as tight as it could go, gave the firemen eighty streams to halt a massive conflagration on a whole front.

On one front. On other fronts the fires rolled on, but in each of these instances, a whole section of a big city was saved. And this story has been repeated in many great fires. It is fights such as these that warm the heart of every man who follows the fire game. As he tells of such episodes, or hears of them, there is a sparkle in his eyes and a smile on his lips.

Not only in conflagrations is there a story of battles that are won or lost. It is an oft-repeated story of a fireman's life. He is frequently termed a firefighter, an apt description, for when his apparatus rolls, he is on his way into battle.

So this book tells of battles. It tells, too, the causes of these disasters, in the hope that a better understanding of causes may lead to a reduction in the vast destruction by fire. More knowledge among citizens in general may help prevent ghastly tragedies such as the Cocoanut Grove, the Iroquois Theater, the apartment house and hotel fires described in these pages.

The fire game, as some call it, is a part of life where there is still romance. This is not always understood by practical and sensible men, who often consider that a fire engine is properly a toy for a small boy.

This romance, this excitement is not confined to sparks and buffs. Firemen of long experience still feel it. The essence of the fire game to us is summed up in a brief scene, a moment of time. In the western part of the city a tannery was afire; going good, as firemen term it. Second and third alarms came quickly on the heels of the first. When the flames burst through the roof, sending burning embers streaming downwind, the general alarm, ten blows, was sounded, summoning every piece of fire apparatus in the city.

We were headed for the fire, down a long, broad street, and a mile ahead lay an enormous towering cloud of black smoke with an angry red glow at its base. Behind us we heard the siren of a fire engine, a company from the far eastern end of the city summoned by the general alarm.

Traffic pulled to the side of the street, the engine flashed by at top speed. The siren, one of the old-fashioned kind that operates with a small hand crank, was emitting one continuous scream. The captain, turning the crank as fast as he could, was not sitting on the front seat, he was standing, tensely leaning over the dashboard, his gaze fixed on the great smoke cloud of this general alarm fire.

He turned the crank unceasingly, as if to speed his engine a bit more, the excitement of the moment gripping him just as much as it did the boys who were racing along the sidewalk toward the fire. He wanted to be there. He wanted to lay a line, hook up his engine to a hydrant, get in there and hit this big one with a strong straight stream from his pump.

A dirty job lay ahead, a dangerous job with perhaps a fast ambulance ride to the hospital to end it. The captain of the engine was not thinking about that. A general alarm fire was burning. He wanted to hit it. Now.

Contents

Illustrations

GENERAL ALARM

1

Evolution of a Fire Department

THE EARLY SETTLERS who came to Boston in 1630 and in the years following knew they had to hurry to get some sort of shelter built for themselves before winter set in. A winter in New England is much more severe than in Old England; a time of year when howling blizzards and savage cold spells may be expected any day.

With almost no building supplies from the home country, the settlers had to use materials available here to men with tools and tremendous energy. They cut wood from the nearby forests; they made thatched roofs of straw and the branches of trees. Lacking bricks, they made chimneys of mud or clay reinforced with sticks of wood. If the inside of the chimney, the flue, was skillfully plastered with mud or clay, it well took care of the smoke and heat from the roaring wood fire a settler needed in the depths of a New England winter.

It was in these early years that the settlers learned that the rugged winter was not the only enemy in this new land they had come to claim as their own. Shelter and warmth they had to have, or endure real suffering in the bitter winter weather of this climate. Their hastily built little thatch-roofed structures gave them shelter, and the limitless supply of fuel from the forests gave them warmth in the worst of weather.

Their other enemy was, the settlers discovered, fire. Fire, that same element which by its grateful warmth made it possible to endure the rigors of winter, became a treacherous enemy ever likely to get beyond control and lay waste months of some man's hard labor by flattening his house. And sometimes the houses of several of the settlers were wiped out by the roaring flames.

Why the element fire so easily managed to escape beyond the control of man is a question easily answered. After winter had gone and the thick blanket of snow had melted off the roof, the thatch of straw and branches dried out under the spring sun; sparks and embers floated up the chimney and dropped onto the dry thatch. Or the mud and clay flaked off the inside of the chimney, leaving the wooden sticks exposed. The result was inevitable; a crackling, flaming thatch or a chimney belching flame and sparks, and another settler without a home.

Boston was growing in importance as the center of the tide of settlers coming to the new country and pushing on to make homes for themselves in eastern Massachusetts. Every year there were more buildings in the town. Something had to be done to check these all too frequent fires. The first step the town of Boston took in the battle against fire was to forbid thatched roofs and chimneys built of wood and clay.

The town meeting also voted that any man who had a chimney fire must pay a fine of ten shillings. Such a fire might originate in the wooden sticks of which the chimney frame was built before the clay or mud was plastered on. Or it might start in the layer of creosote and soot which always collects in a chimney where wood is burned. This creosote can make a fierce fire that shoots sparks into the sky and, of course, onto the owner's roof and onto the roofs of his neighbors. The householder was bound to see to it that he had no chimney fires from any cause. To fail meant a ten-shilling fine, a substantial sum in those days. As a result, great care was exercised to see that the flue of the chimney was well plastered at all times and also free of creosote and soot.

Here were three moves toward fire protection, the first steps in this primitive colonial town. And at this time there was a bucket brigade which at each fire consisted of everyone in the vicinity who could lay hands on a receptacle that would hold water.

But fire protection did not keep pace with the growth of prospering colonial Boston. Each year settlers arrived in great numbers, the harbor was excellent, commerce increased, Boston was the center of trade and business for a score of towns along the bay and it was the capital of the province. The number of buildings increased. Hazards increased. Fire protection did not increase.

In 1654, twenty-three years after the first settlement, the inevitable happened. A sweeping fire, a conflagration, struck Boston, raged entirely out of control in the center of town where State, Washington, and Devonshire streets now lie. Three people were killed, many buildings were destroyed with their contents, and a heavy blow was dealt the business life of the town.

This severe lesson resulted in a series of laws that greatly strengthened the protection of the town. These were basic laws, so important in the evolution of the science of fire protection that they should be enumerated here.

1. Every house was required to have a ladder or ladders long enough to reach the ridge pole.

This was an excellent counter move in the campaign to prevent roof fires. If the house could be laddered, the owner and his neighbors could get at a roof fire at once, use water and dirt, or tear away the burning part and throw it to the ground. In the past, with no means to get to the roof, they had to stand helplessly as the growing flames mounted up into the sky.

2. Every house was obliged to have a twelve-foot pole with a swob on the end. The use of this in extinguishing a roof fire is obvious. A man standing on the ground might reach much of the roof and from a short ladder he could probably reach all of it. As for wetting the swob, finding enough liquid to moisten it sufficiently would not occasion any difficulty for most men.

3. It was voted that the town should have six "good and long" ladders to be hung on the outside of the meeting house. These were the equivalent of the modern ladder company, for distances were not great and a few men could quickly bring the ladders to the scene of the fire for rescue work or for getting onto the roof.

The town meeting had contemplated the possibility that painters or carpenters might borrow the ladders and thus they would be missing at the moment of need. Therefore, it was voted that the ladders be branded with the town mark and a fine of twenty shillings be imposed on anyone who removed the ladders except in case of fire.

4. It was ordered that four "good, strong iron crooks" with chains and ropes attached and fastened to poles were to hang at the side of the meeting house.

These were used in a technique unknown today; the tearing away of a structure near the burning building so the fire could not spread. In the twentieth century this method has been used in the country where house and barn are connected by a long, low woodshed and either house or barn is afire. If water is scarce and the connecting shed is ripped away, the fire can be prevented from traveling along what wood is left by one stream of water, or, lacking that, by a determined bucket brigade.

5. The town of Boston established a cistern, or conduit, at the corner of State and Exchange streets so that a water supply might be readily at hand. Steps were taken to see that buckets were available. This was the first step in the direction of a public water supply for fire purposes.

6. It was forbidden by law to build a fire within three rods of any building.

This is an elementary precaution, although often disregarded even today. Thoughtless people, particularly suburbanites, make rubbish fires in the open, then stroll into the house for a cookie and a glass of ginger ale. With a puff of wind, an ember lodges in combustible material such as dry grass and the fire is away. By the time the glass of ginger ale is finished it is time to pull the box.

7. For arson the penalty was death. The early settlers did not trifle with serious offenders; it was a rugged age. In 1681

a woman set fire to a dwelling house and in the blaze one of the occupants perished. The savage retribution for this crime was the sentence that the culprit be publicly burned to death.

8. The town meeting passed a law making it illegal to carry burning brands from one house to another, except in a safe vessel "to secure it from the winds."

To us today this may seem a very curious matter to be the subject of a law carrying a stiff fine. Yet, understanding those early colonial times, the reason for the law is readily apparent. There were no matches in those days. Therefore, one whose fire was out had to start it again by other methods.

The Indians made a fire by rotating a small round stick in a hole in a piece of punky wood until the shreds of wood smoldered from the heat of friction. Then they blew on it until it glowed, put on straw and splinters, blew some more, and at last had fire. This was a tedious operation requiring a high degree of skill and patience.

More frequently used was the tinder box and the flint and steel. From a metal box was taken a handful of inflammables: threads, splinters, shavings. Then with the flint and steel the settler would try to strike sparks that would ignite this collection of light stuff. A pinch of gunpowder sprinkled on the tinder made the procedure much easier, although a man needed to be alert lest the flash of the powder scorch off his beard and his eyebrows.

Rather than fiddle with the Indian method or the flint and steel, some settlers would load a musket with a powder charge but no bullet, hold the muzzle of the gun near a pile of tinder in the fireplace, and squeeze the trigger. The blast of the gun set the tinder ablaze and that was an end of the matter; the settler had his fire.

However, this used gunpowder, which was precious. The easy way to start a fire was to skip over to a neighbor's house with a dish and borrow a few glowing embers. Of course, one who did this might be obliged to listen to a little "sass" on the subject of people so shiftless as to allow the fire to go out. But the time saved made taking some remarks worthwhile.

If, on the way back with the glowing embers, the wind whisked some of them out of the dish and into the dry grass or under the hen house, there was trouble. Fire from this cause must have been frequent if the town meeting considered legislation necessary. Perhaps a householder hurried so as to be away from the remarks of the one from whom he had borrowed, and failed to notice that he had spilled a glowing coal or that the wind had taken it. And, if he hurried, he might fall flat on his face and spill the whole business.

The problem was taken care of by the new law requiring that the dish be "secure from the winds." A covered dish, in other words.

9. The town established a night patrol. These were the bellmen, on duty from midnight until five in the morning, a time when honest men were supposed to be in bed. They detected a fire starting in the night. Such a fire would have progressed unobserved until of really dangerous magnitude, for those were days when to be "abroad in the nighttime without giving a good account" of oneself was a crime. The patrol, upon seeing any unusual light, at once gave the alarm. This today is a duty performed by the night shift of the police, and those who read accounts of fires have noted how frequently an alarm for a fire in the small hours is turned in by a police officer.

10. No fires were allowed in vessels at the wharves, a rule enforced by officers termed water bailiffs.

These ten laws were excellent fire-prevention legislation; positive evidence that the colonial Americans well realized that something must be done to make a closely built town more safe from fire. Yet the conflagration of 1653 resulted in no improvement in the means for actually fighting fires. The bucket brigade was still the only force that fought a fire that had started.

But Boston was thinking about fighting fires. It was at this time that the town ordered a fire engine from Joseph Jencks, yet no record can be found that he ever delivered it. Possibly Jencks thought he could manufacture a fire engine and discovered that he lacked the mechanical skill and ability to carry his ideas into effect. Mechanical and engineering capability was very scarce in those days, more so than we of today realize. In that era the principle of the pump was known, but equipment to manufacture such a machine was almost nonexistent. Experience in designing parts that would work efficiently together was lacking and there were few trained mechanics. Today an idea can be put into practical execution swiftly and with certainty because trained engineers, draftsmen, and mechanics are readily available and proper materials and machinery may be procured without difficulty.

Other excellent fire-safety measures were developed in this period. A reservoir twelve feet square was constructed near Faneuil Hall and supplied with water conveyed to it through wooden pipes from nearby springs and wells. Those who had chimneys not conforming to law were given official warnings.

In 1670 a law was enacted requiring every building owner to have an open hogshead of water outside near his door.

This he was required to do from March 1 to November 1. Why he was excused from November 1 to February 28 does not appear. Maybe it was thought the water in the hogshead would freeze in winter and be of no use in case of fire. More likely, however, is that the hogshead of water was ordered for use on any roof fire that might start from chimney sparks and in the winter the roofs of the town were so much of the time wet with rains or covered with snow that spark danger was not a problem.

With their bucket brigades and more stringent fire-prevention laws and better sources of water, the people of Boston were masters of the fire situation for years. In 1672 they managed what firemen today call a good stop. Two dwellings and a warehouse were ablaze on a dry windy day and the wind was carrying a storm of glowing sparks and burning brands down to leeward in the closely built town. We wish that details of this valiant fight were preserved for us in some observer's written account. But we have only the notation "the inhabitants by their promptness and their hard work got the fire under control."

In 1676, twenty-three years after the first conflagration, another general fire made a gaping hole in busy Boston. This one consumed forty-six dwellings, several warehouses, and the North Meeting House in the district bounded by Hanover, Clark, and Richmond streets. This fire was controlled only when a rainstorm commenced.

With this disaster as an impetus, Boston took another forward step. The Newsham fire engine, manufactured in England, was known to be capable of delivering a stream of water. In 1678 Boston purchased one.

This first piece of mechanical fire apparatus, then termed a water engine, was a rectangular box or tub into which the bucket brigade poured water while the men on the pump handles supplied pressure. On the engine was mounted a big nozzle or goose neck much like the deck gun on modern fire apparatus.

The engine was placed in front of the burning building, and the big nozzle shot a stream into the fire. This was a great advance. Instead of men throwing water at a fire which they might or might not reach, and with each one throwing the water as he thought best, there was one stream pointed into the seat of the fire. The stream was fairly steady. It had force and enough pressure to carry the water to an upper window or to the roof.

This Newsham engine was really the first hand tub. Many refinements were made as time went on, and it was this type of apparatus that carried the burden of American fire fighting for a century and a half. Then steam took over.

But one engine was not enough for Boston. In 1679 another fire got entirely out of hand, destroying eighty dwellings and seventy warehouses in twelve hours as it worked from one building to another.

After this blow, a further drastic strengthening of the building laws was enacted. All new buildings must be of stone or brick and all roofs of slate or tile. This was severe legislation for those early days.

Yet here again, with this strong new building law we find no measures to increase Boston's ability to fight a fire that had gained a foothold. More bad fires followed. The town did buy two more English fire engines in 1707. Not nearly enough, it would seem, for in 1711 another fire got completely away from the force Boston could muster to fight it.

This time over one hundred buildings from Cornhill to the harbor front were leveled.

Boston continued to try to meet this dreadfully destructive problem. This time the Provincial Legislature enacted a statute authorizing the appointment of officials called firewards who had the power to command assistance from anyone to fight fire, remove property, and stand guard against looters. For disobeying the orders of a fireward, the penalty was a forty-shilling fine or ten days in jail.

After the fire of 1711, the town bought three more engines, bringing the total to six. In 1739 the town commenced to pay firemen. In addition, there was an award of five pounds to the engine company that got first water on the fire. By 1740 the number of engines had been increased to nine.

If the people of Boston thought their many excellent fire-prevention laws and their nine water engines were adequate to meet the fire menace, they received a discouraging shock on March 20, 1760. Again a fire started on Cornhill, and marched through what are now Washington, State, Congress, Devonshire, Kilby, and Water streets to the harbor. With a northwest gale driving the flames, it was impossible for the firemen to face the fierce heat in front of the fire. It stopped only when it reached the salt water, having consumed four hundred buildings.

What did the nine fire engines imported from England do this day? They performed well. The sweeping fire was confined at its sides; it did not spread in either a northerly or a southerly direction, which it probably would have done had it not been for the nine good streams from the hand tubs. That was a victory in the gallant fight the firemen put up that day. Nevertheless, the fire was the worst that had occurred in colonial America to that date.

Immediately one asks what advances in fire protection resulted from this painful lesson.

First, there was legislation requiring wider streets. It may come as a surprise to visitors from other cities to learn that Boston's streets were even narrower than they now are, but indeed they were. This narrowness was one factor in the conflagrations that ravaged the town, for intense heat radiating from a burning building easily crosses a street that is no more than a lane. Then, unless there are strong streams at that point, both sides of the thoroughfare are ablaze.

Second, the laws requiring stone and brick in buildings and slate on the roofs were strengthened.

Yet, it was not until two years later that another fire engine, the tenth, was acquired. The amount of power available to meet a bad fire was considerably increased in this year 1762 by another move, the first use of what today is known as mutual aid.

At a bad fire in a bakery in 1762 which required all ten of Boston's pumping engines, they were assisted by an engine from Castle William and an engine from Charlestown. Some years later, in a fire involving the entire block of Congress, Milk, Pearl, and Purchase streets, the fire, which might easily have become a conflagration, was mastered by the Boston engines and apparatus from Cambridge, Charlestown, Roxbury, Brookline, Milton, and Watertown. It is well recognized today that out-of-town engines can spell the difference between a fire that is controlled and a fire that gets away.

The year 1802 marked a great advance in the art of firefighting; the introduction of lead hose, which was hose leading from the engine to the fire. Suction was taken from a well or cistern or conduit or one of the newly installed hydrants, and the water was pumped through the leading hose to the fire. There the hosemen held the nozzle, directing the stream at the fire. If they wished to move to a more advantageous position, they could drag the hose. They could enter an alley with their hose line and fight from a spot too narrow for their engine to enter. Or they could enter the building. This was a great step forward.

By 1825 all the engines had leading hose and could take suction. The hose system was a great relief to the firewards, those officials upon whom had rested the duty of commanding citizens to work in the bucket brigades that carried water from the source and poured it into the engine located in front of the burning building. Although they were vested with legal authority to impress men, it had become increasingly difficult to find enough men to operate the bucket lines. It was hard, sloppy, unromantic work and spectators managed to avoid the firewards seeking men. With the engine at the source of water, the bucket lines were no longer necessary.

Completion in 1849 of water pipes bringing water from Lake Cochituate made possible a hydrant system as we know it today. The pressure was excellent and four hose wagons were added, each carrying 1800 feet of hose and some axes and buckets. Many smaller fires could be handled by a hose company.

The first hook and ladder companies were activated in 1820. Previously ladders were kept at certain locations for fire use, it being thought they were too long and cumbersome to be carried on a vehicle. By 1820 engineering had reached the point where a long carriage to carry hooks, ladders, and tools could be constructed. The hook from which this apparatus took part of its original designation was not a plaster hook, but a much larger tool used in tearing down a building standing in the path of the flames or in opening up a structure already ablaze.

Enormous numbers of men were needed to operate the fire department in those days. Men pulled the heavy apparatus to the fire, men worked the pumps. No horses, no steam, no motors; manpower did it all.

There were no permanent firemen. They were all call men who dropped their work and headed for the engine house when the bells sounded the alarm. The first to arrive at the house took hold of the drag ropes and got the old machine rolling, and as more men caught up and got a grip on the ropes they worked up to a dead run with their apparatus. To see a hand tub come down the street with fifty men on the ropes, bell ringing, and everyone shouting was an unforgettable sight.

If a man stumbled and fell, he rolled out of the way if he were lucky. If he were not, he was run over by the heavy engine. This could be a fatality; some are recorded. If the thermometer was ninety-eight in the shade, he ran to the engine house, took hold of the drag ropes, and ran with his machine. If the thermometer were ten below zero and the hour after midnight, he jumped from his warm bed, struggled into his clothes, and ran for the engine house.

This labor was not done for money. It was done for the honor of a man's engine company. Zero weather, falling walls, hot weather, and physical exhaustion were borne because the engine company meant a very great deal to its men.

It was an honor to belong. And these men loved the fire-fighting game.)

The fire companies held picnics and clambakes and dances and banquets and all manner of social functions. Each man was determined that his company should be the best, so it was not strange that intense rivalries grew.

The Boston men were normal American firemen of that day. In 1767 it was recorded that several of the companies "played their engines upon one another." This was a good water fight and no heads were broken, but it is probable that the fire itself did not get the attention it deserved until someone in authority put a stop to this and managed to get the streams directed at the burning building.

It was in the mid-nineteenth century that the fire companies, growing in political strength and in pride and in feelings of rivalry, really began to be a problem. In this era Boston's Engine 2 company was discharged "on account of disgraceful conduct." The records do not disclose what the conduct was. There are several references to companies being disbanded for misconduct and unbecoming conduct. Again, specifications are lacking.

Fights, riots, and insubordination were common. In the Tremont Theatre a grand brawl occurred between rival factions that almost wrecked the theater.

Another disciplinary difficulty in handling the large engine companies resulted from the simple fact that these men had joined the department because they loved to fight fire. When a bad fire occurred in a nearby town, such as Cambridge or Charlestown or Roxbury, the men of the various companies would see it and head for their engine houses. If it still looked promising, they were likely to roll without waiting for an order from the chief and upon arrival they turned to with a will to assist the neighboring town to get the situation in hand. This was another adventure; they loved it.

This thirst for action on the part of the firemen several times resulted in a serious lack of coverage in Boston because so many of the companies, without orders, had departed to fight a big one in some neighboring town. The chief directed the firewards to post themselves on the road out of Boston when there was a serious fire in a nearby community and when four Boston companies had passed, to turn back all other companies heading for the out-of-town fire. Thus Boston itself would have enough apparatus left for its own protection.

Upon one such occasion Engine 8 got into real trouble. Headed for a big column of black smoke in Roxbury, they were intercepted by one of the firewards and ordered back to quarters. The men, well on their way to what appeared to be an excellent fire, did not take kindly to this interruption by higher authority. There was considerable hard language and thumbing of noses. Engine 8 continued on to the fire and the firemen had the soul-satisfying experience of helping the Roxbury boys get the threatening fire out.

But that was not an end of the matter. The fireward who had been defied carried this insubordination to the highest authority. The foreman and the chief clerk of Engine 8 were discharged and the rest of the company were given an ear-tingling lecture on obeying orders.

The tempting money prize for the first company to get water on the fire led to another problem. In the earlier times before hydrants and leading hose, when an engine arrived at a fire the men had to wait until the bucket brigade had poured in water before they could start to pump and get a stream on the burning structure.

Some brilliant fellow conceived the idea of keeping a hundred gallons or so of water in the tub of the engine as it stood in the house awaiting an alarm. His company, as soon as it "got in there," as firemen phrase it, was able to start pumping immediately, hoping the bucket brigade would begin to get water to them before their hundred gallons was gone. The company walked off with the prize for first water a few times before the other companies caught on and started doing the same thing.

The problem arose with winter's first severe cold. The water in the tubs of engines standing in unheated quarters froze. When a frozen engine reached a fire it had ice in the intake and ice in the tub. The engine was useless. So a rule was issued forbidding water in the tub or cistern of an engine until arrival at the fire.

The year 1853 marked a great step in the evolution of the Boston Fire Department, and indeed, in every big-city fire department. A committee was appointed to visit the Latta Works in Cincinnati to view the steam fire engines being manufactured there. They watched the sample engine work, returned to Boston, and recommended purchase.

The first Boston steamer, named *Miles Greenwood,* was a disappointment for purely practical reasons. It was too big, heavy, and cumbersome for work in Boston, where many streets do not have the width common in newer places. The chief asked for smaller steamers and got them.

This was the turning point. By 1860 the entire department was equipped with steamers, hose wagons, and horses. In 1864 the first fire boat went in service, equipped with two steam pumps and for some curious reason operating under the jurisdiction of the police department.

Everyone in Boston was immensely proud of their new fire department and proud, too, of the new fire-alarm system. This was an electric telegraph connected with boxes well placed about the city. It was not as easy to "pull the box" then as it is today, for the authorities were obsessed with the idea that light-minded people would play with this new fire-alarm equipment and cause the department many needless runs. So a fire-alarm box could be opened only with a key which was kept at a nearby house or store.

This resulted in something worse than any number of false alarms; namely, a delayed alarm. Few things are more undesirable in the view of fire-protection engineers than a delayed alarm, so, at their urging, the old key system was abandoned, the present type of box was adopted, and anyone caught sending in a false alarm got a trip to the police station.

In 1864, when the Civil War was raging, a Russian naval squadron visited some of our ports to show the world that Russia favored the Union cause. The British and French openly favored the Confederacy, so much so that it was feared they might intervene and furnish the South with military assistance. Russia, smarting from a defeat by Britain and France in the Crimean War in the previous decade, sent a naval squadron to American east coast ports to embarrass the British and the French. This it did.

The mayor of Boston, as part of the city's effort to give the Russians the very best in entertainment, grouped the naval officers at a particular point, and told them as best he could what to expect. Then he pulled the box. Shortly there was a tremendous uproar from several directions and the apparatus came galloping onto the scene, bells ringing, steamer whistles blowing, smoke pouring from the stacks, helmeted firemen clinging to running boards and steps. Although it is not recorded, one may guess that word had been passed beforehand for a double response to this one.

This form of entertainment was used on other occasions. A commission from St. Louis visiting Boston was accorded this honor, and the Queen of Hawaii and her entourage were given the opportunity of seeing the apparatus arrive. While the St. Louis people doubtless had seen this sort of thing before, one can easily picture the astonishment of the Russian officers and Her Majesty at this look at the Boston department in all its glory.

Soon after the development of the steamer came the first chemical engine, a two-horse vehicle carrying two fifty-gallon tanks of a soda and acid preparation that gave a strong stream through a one-inch hose when the operator turned the crank that tipped the sulphuric acid bottle so that its contents ran into the bicarbonate of soda solution in the tanks. These small streams were used on closet fires, on fires in rooms and partitions, or on a wooden shingle roof. It is probable that chemical lines extinguished a good half of the fires to which the department was called.

These light lines caused less water damage than a two-and-a-half-inch water line, and one man could handle the hose and easily get into odd corners, such as in an attic. It used to be thought that the carbon dioxide gas, the pressure of which pushed the liquid through the hose, was of value in helping to smother the fire. This gas may have been of value in an enclosed space such as a closet or inside a partition, but today little weight is given this factor. In modern fire departments, small fires are handled by light water lines given their pressure by a rotary pump powered by the motor of the apparatus.

The water tower was another development in the age of steam. This piece of apparatus, used only in big fires, takes as many as six engine lines at connections at the bottom, and delivers one massive and powerful stream into a window in an upper story of a burning building.

In Boston, a landmark in the evolution of the fire department was the conflagration of 1872. Other cities have had conflagrations, and lessons have been learned from them; painful lessons. The conflagration of 1872 deserves its own chapter, and will be discussed later.

After these developments of the second half of the nineteenth century, we find no outstanding event in the evolution of the fire department until the early years of the twentieth century, when the development of the gasoline motor brought to an end the era of fire horses. These beautiful and beloved animals took their departure, leaving behind them a sadness in the hearts of old-time firemen.

The men had lived with their horses and cared for them and ridden behind them over the years. They took pride in the speed with which their horses came out of the stalls when the tapper hit. They boasted of how swiftly their horses took the heavy engines to the fire, and they told the men of other companies that they were unfortunate in not having horses as strong and as fast and as handsome. No motor, with its sputtering and smells and, above all, its lack of a soul, could take the place of horses in the affections of an old-time fireman.

It is interesting to note that the gasoline motor supplanted horses but did not supersede steam until many years later.

Here again, the answer lies in the capability of the mechanical engineers. A motor vehicle for a hose wagon, a chemical engine, or even a ladder was quite possible. But engineers were not at first successful in making a motor truck with a shift that would transfer the gasoline engine's power from the task of taking the fire apparatus to the fire to the task of driving the pump.

Early efforts to accomplish this were unreliable. Failures and breakdowns were frequent, so a fire chief at all familiar with developments demanded steam. To take the steamer to the fire a motorized tractor was fitted onto the front and thus the motive power was supplied to the front wheels. So with these tractors the steamer came lumbering onto the fire scene, trailing smoke and sparks as it always had. It usually arrived well behind the lighter and faster hose wagon.

Engineering continued to make forward strides and gradually motor pumps of great power and reliability were developed. They came in time to replace the motorized steamers as they wore out. The steam fire engine, in itself a noble and picturesque creation full of vitality and action as it worked, gradually became a museum piece, and today the motor-pumping engine is in universal use.

2

The Days of the Hand Tub

AS AMERICAN CITIES grew, the need for more fire apparatus increased until in the mid-nineteenth century the number of hand-operated fire engines was enormous. The first crude water engines imported from England were followed by a succession of improved models developed in America. Hose was added, and hose reels responded to each alarm along with the engine. While the engine was rolled into position at a well, brook, cistern, or hydrant to take suction, a line was laid from the hose reel to the fire.

No longer was a bucket brigade required to pour water into a trap door at the top of the tub. The engine took suction as does the modern apparatus of today. If the water source was so far from the fire that the water lost pressure by being pushed through too long a line of hose, the method of relaying was used to give the men at the fire with the brass play pipe a strong, effective stream. The engine drafting the water laid out all its hose and pumped into the box of another engine whose hose led to the fire, or possibly into the box of the third engine, which pumped to the fire.

Fortunate it was that the suction pipe replaced the bucket brigade as a means of getting water into the box or chamber of the engine. All the manpower was needed to work the handles or brakes of the pumping engine. As the design was improved over the years, the small handles on the early machine were lengthened in later models until they ran the entire length of the engine, providing room for fifteen or more men on each side. They worked at speed to give as strong a stream as possible, a man-killing job that usually wore the crew down to the point of exhaustion in a matter of twenty minutes.

When one crew was completely worn out, a fresh crew was put at the brakes, while the first men were allowed to rest and have refreshments, some of which came from a brown jug. The stream produced by one of these hand engines was, for most purposes, a good one. Those who doubt this statement should attend a modern Fireman's Muster where a dozen or more of the old hand tubs, every one of them more than a hundred years old, compete for prizes. The machines are kept in first-class mechanical condition by these enthusiasts. The engines are transported on motor trucks to the town where the Muster is to be held. There is a parade of the apparatus, led by a brass band, and in the line of march are numerous pieces of modern fire apparatus, a couple of drum and bugle corps, and more bands.

At a playground they hold their contest. The men and boys work the brakes with a prodigious thumping of the mechanism, and the foreman stands on top yelling encouragement and earthy exhortations. The stream lances out to the measuring area, where paper is laid to show where the farthest drops land. After a few minutes they stop and the judges measure the length of the stream and record it in their book. Surprising as the power of these streams is, it is obvious on a moment's reflection that the motor pump can continue to deliver its strong, powerful stream for three hours or all day, if need be, whereas the men at the brakes of a hand tub must be rested before they have pumped a half hour.

It was the great need for manpower that was at once the glory and the downfall of the hand tubs of the mid-nineteenth century. The firemen were volunteers, they were unpaid, and they were recruited in numbers sufficient to operate the large numbers of engines by the idea that it was an honor to belong to the fire company.

There were many good times connected with being a fireman; picnics, dances, clambakes, parades. Then there was the fun of being at a fire, an enjoyment common in most healthy males of the species. These men were requited for the tremendous and unpaid labors demanded of them at a big fire by the honor accorded a fireman. But above all, it was the sense of belonging, the *esprit de corps* of their fire company, the pride they had in their beautiful machine and the game of it all.

Every fire is a challenge and they gloried in meeting the fire and fighting it. It is to be remembered that a fireman is most often referred to as a fire-fighter and one who worked at a big one says "I fought at that fire."

It was in the rivalry with other fire companies that the competitive spirit of the male human really came to the fore. His engine was the best; his company was the best, the

Library
I.U.P.
Indiana, Pa.

628.92 H336g
c.1

strongest, the smartest, and performed best at the fire. When long lines were necessary and they relayed, one engine pumping into another, the first engine tried to pump hard enough to deliver more water into the box of the second engine than its crew could pump out into the hose leading to the fire. This filled the box of the second engine and caused the water to overflow and wet the feet of the men working the brakes.

When the first engine had "washed" the second, the two-score men of the first hand tub's crew stopped pumping to cheer and slap one another on the back, and those who were not actually on the brakes skipped down the road to shout insults at the company that had been washed. Generally a number of fist fights took place on the spot and many others in the days following, as the members of the first engine's company went about town bragging about the disgrace of the second engine company in being washed.

Pride, rivalries, fights, involvement in politics, large groups of volunteer firemen getting more and more out of hand; all this dimmed the glory of the age of the superb hand tubs and the happy but riotous life their men led. With increasing frequency the fights took place at the scene of the fire.

Sometimes, at night, when an engine company feared the disgrace of being washed by another engine that was pumping into it, a man with a sharp knife was sent back to cut the hose where it passed through a dark and unlighted spot.

Because of these turbulent episodes a fire that should have been confined to the building of origin often got out of hand and spread. The firemen were engaged in fighting each other instead of the fire. This fierce manly competition was creating conditions that were to result in far-reaching changes.

To give reality to the situation, here is an account of a

typical instance as it might have occurred, in 1853. The following description of the fire in Sweetser's Mill tells the story of the hand fire engines and their men at the very height of their development; it shows their strength and their weaknesses and gives us a look at the time to come.

Cool, with a brisk breeze from the northwest, it was fine weather for the ball that Cataract 8's boys were putting on in the old Lyceum Hall this October night in 1853. That fire company had 80 men and for weeks every one in it had been working like a beaver to make this party a success. And one of the things 8's men set out to make sure of was that none of the members of the other fire companies got in.

They did pretty well at guarding the doors of the hall, and they needed to. There was a lot of rivalry among the dozen hand tubs in town and plenty of arguments as to which engine could throw the longest stream, which crew of men could pump the longest, who had the best paint job or brasswork or firehouse or clambake or corn roast or picnic or dance.

Cataract 8's boys were a long way toward showing everyone in town that no dance was ever as good as theirs, and the other fire companies, most of whom had been bested by 8 in various ways, were not happy about it. The crowd hanging around outside got bigger and bigger; there were men there from Big 6 and Reliance 1, Torrent 2 and the Four Leaf Clover, and the other companies.

It was during the third number the fight started, no one knows just why, but probably when a few men from some of the other companies tried to push past the guards that Cataract 8 had at the door. On one thing everyone agreed; it was the best fight the town's fire companies ever had. That was saying a lot, because they fought regularly—sometimes at the fire, when one company got to a well or a cistern just ahead of another; sometimes on the way to the fire, when, racing neck and neck, one brushed against the other, damaging its paint; and there was generally a battle when one company had a social occasion and the others butted in.

But this was the biggest fight. The orchestra packed up and left in a hurry, the ladies huddled over in one corner of the hall screaming, chairs got broken, the big lights of glass in the windows went crashing into the street, the police came and were swallowed up in the howling, fist-swinging mob. And everyone was having a wonderful time; this sort of thing was part of being a fireman, even if some of the unlucky ones had to be carried to the doctor's office on a shutter.

Things happen by chance, and so one might say it was chance that old man Sweetser went down to his mill that evening to catch up on his bookkeeping. The little office was cold and Mr. Sweetser, who was not a patient man, proceeded to warm the room up fast by putting a handful of shavings and a bushel of pine kindling into the pot-bellied stove. Then he touched a match to it and settled down to his ledgers, only to find that he had left the sheets with last week's transactions on his bureau at home. Muttering, he went back to the house for them.

The fire of pine kindling warmed the little office, just as he had intended. The stove pipe turned cherry red. The partition where the pipe entered the chimney began to smoke, and the ends of the laths, much too near the metal, glowed and commenced to burn. By the time old man Sweetser returned from his home the windows of the office were scarlet;

smoke spurted out of all the cracks and rose up the side of the building.

He made a quick decision. He could not move very swiftly, yet he got up to Ezra Walden's house in pretty good time, and stamped in without knocking.

"I want Ezra."

"He ain't feeling well," replied Martha, nodding toward the bedroom.

"My mill is afire," shouted Mr. Sweetser. "It's his job to ring the fire bell, isn't it?"

"Yes, but he's runnin' a fever. I'll ring it."

She did. Running to the church nearby, she unlocked the front door, reached for the bell rope, and hauled with all her strength. Six blows she sounded, hanging on the rope each time, her feet off the floor, to make sure the heavy clapper hit the bell. Six blows for a fire in the Sixth Ward. She paused for breath and rang another six and still another and when she came out in the cold night air, breathless, the other bells of the town had taken up the count; some near, some in the far distance, six blows for a fire in the Sixth Ward. Down at the end of the street, in the hollow, the sky was red now, for the fire had burst the windows and was climbing the side of Sweetser's Mill.

Downtown, at the Lyceum Hall, no one heard the first bell. Things were far too noisy; shouts, the crash of breaking glass, the tramp of feet as the fighting crowd punched it out on the dance floor, in the street, and on the stairways drowned out any other sound. But someone on his way to the fight, running, was still far enough away from the uproar to hear the six strokes of the bell. He ran faster.

"Fire in the Sixth Ward," he bellowed, charging into the

crowd. "Man your engines. Fire in the Sixth Ward. The bells are ringing."

The battle ceased immediately. The crowd came pouring out into the street, running toward their engine houses, some with bloody noses and clothes half torn off. Buggies and wagons loaded with men galloped off to some of the firehouses, but most had to run. The doors of the firehouses were swung open. The men laid hold of the drag ropes and the heavy engines rolled. No more guide was needed than that dull red glow in the western sky.

The department got down to Sweetser's Mill in fairly good time, considering that most of the men knew nothing about the fire until the bells had been ringing a while and then had to run all the way to their engine houses before they could get their machines started. Some of the houses were a good two miles from The Lyceum Hall where Cataract 8's ball had begun and ended.

Only the Four Leaf Clover had trouble getting there. They turned into Federal Street at the same moment as Alert 5. There was considerable shouting back and forth, they raced, bets were made on the spot, and the two companies charged down the middle of the road as tight as they could go. When Alert 5 pulled ahead a bit, the foreman of the Four Leaf Clover ordered his men to take to the sidewalk, which was some smoother. They gained, and it looked like a dead heat until Four's right rear wheel struck an elm tree and collapsed.

Alert 5's crew, booing and cat-calling, went on to the fire at top speed, while Four's men took off the smashed wheel and dragged their engine along with the end of the axle leaving a furrow in the street. They were really late, the last company to get to work, and the chief had a lot to say. That did not bother Four's men much. Everyone was late to this fire; everyone was in bad with the chief.

The department's response to this alarm of fire was very poor, and the chief knew he would hear from the selectmen in the morning. The Sweetser Mill was going from one end to the other, and only one of his engines had a line on it. Enterprise 11, whose men had been having a quiet whist party in their own quarters, had rolled when the bell first sounded and were drafting from Caleb Wiley's well. All their men were present and working on the long brakes that powered the machine; up and down, up and down, with a moderate stroke that punched a fine stream of water through the line of leather hose.

Standing on top of the engine, Enterprise 11's foreman beat out the rhythm with his brass speaking trumpet, sometimes waving it in the air like an orchestra leader's baton, occasionally banging it noisily on the gleaming air chamber when he thought his men needed a little encouragement.

"Easy does it. Easy does it," he sang out. "Give her a punch, a punch, a punch. Down and up. Down and up. We're the boys. Well we know it."

Enterprise 11's stream was at an important point between the blazing mill and a large house only a few feet away. The three men holding the play pipe had a strong stream to batter back the fire; they had swung into action just as the flames had started to reach across toward the dwelling house and they were masters of the situation. The chief turned away from Enterprise 11 to roar at the other companies.

One by one they found places from which to draft water; cisterns, wells, Strawberry Brook. They got their lines stretched to the fire and their pumps going until even the Four Leaf Clover, minus a wheel, was in action. The engines rocked back and forth to the mighty efforts of these hundreds of men who now knew they were very much in the wrong. The foremen shouted and banged their speaking trumpets on the brake handles; the streams of Cataract 8 and Reliance 1 and Golden Girl 12 and Big 6 and the others lanced into the rolling flames. Over all that part of the Sixth Ward hung the smell of burning wood and the fragrance of the bubbling chocolate and the cloves and nutmegs and pepper and coffee that Sweetser had in his mill.

But the firemen were too late, very much too late.

Swirling up from the mill a cloud of embers thicker than any snowstorm rose briefly until the wind caught them and swept them down Waterhill Street. Part of the mill roof collapsed, the shower of embers increased, pieces as big as a man's hand, glowing red hot. Down came the clouds of burning brands on the dry wooden shingle roofs all along Waterhill Street. Some lodged in cracks and crevices or lay in incandescent patches on the shingled surfaces; many of the embers rolled down the slopes and into the wooden gutters, filling them with beds of glowing coals hot enough to broil a steak.

The chief saw what he was faced with; a conflagration, a sweeping fire that would march through the town unchecked until it reached open fields at the outskirts. Leaving streams at each side of the mill, he ordered all the companies away from the front of the fire, where the heat was punishing and the fight was hopeless. Their hose lines were laid down Waterhill to cover the rows of dwellings.

This took time. The men had already been in the wild fist

fight at The Lyceum Hall, and then they had run to their engine houses to get their apparatus. They had run down into the Sixth Ward pulling the heavy machines, and after that they had worked on the brakes, pumping furiously. They were exhausted. Some stumbled and fell as they rushed into this new part of the battle against the fire, and when they got their engines going again the beat of the tired men was slower, the streams weaker.

There were so many roof fires now that it looked as if the whole of Waterhill Street was lost and it probably would have been had it not been for the arrival of the Buttercup Engine from nearby Clifton and the Reading Rangers and Waterboy 2 from Barnegat.

No message reached these out-of-town companies; no riders galloped over to call them. They saw the red glow in the sky, they knew they were needed, and they called up their men and started for the fire. Like true firemen they hauled their machines by hand, but before they had gone a mile, better sense won the day and they took advantage of the offer of horses for the long out-of-town run. For a fire in their community, it would have been a disgrace not to have pulled their machine themselves. But they knew this was no time to hold to any such ideas, so they arrived quickly. They had not expended their strength on a six-mile run and they pitched right in.

That is what saved the street—three fresh streams, men ready to monkey up ladders with their axes and chop away the last glowing boards, quick hands shifting hose lines. One by one the fires in the houses were extinguished. Sweetser's Mill by now was dropping apart. The roof was gone, the walls fell in, and at last it was no more than a pile of blazing debris, surrounded by a dozen companies of dog-tired firemen who drenched the ruins with streams that were pumped with a very slow stroke indeed.

Dawn was in the eastern sky when the chief told Golden Girl and Red Rover 10 to pick up and go home. Then he sent the others back to quarters, one by one, Big 6, Reliance 1, the Silver Gray, and the others, keeping only the Four Leaf Clover, because it could not move, and Enterprise 11, whose men he said were the best in town. They were the only ones working at the smoking ruins at breakfasttime when the selectmen came down in a group to have a talk with the chief. The men, some working, some enjoying the hot coffee and doughnuts and apple pie brought out to them by the women of the neighborhood, listened carefully to hear what was said, and they managed to hear most of it, because neither the chief nor the various selectmen made any effort to moderate their voices.

"Well, Chief," began Selectman Burrill, "we lost Sweetser's Mill and there's a dozen houses ain't fit to live in."

"That's right," glumly replied the chief.

"What's your explanation?" queried Selectman Mansfield.

"The wind." said the chief. "A stiff breeze blowing right down Waterhill Street."

Selectman Perkins, a big man with a full beard and a loud booming voice, wagged a finger under the chief's nose.

"That's nonsense and you know it. You can't control your men. They were fighting downtown, nine-tenths of them. They'd rather fight each other than fight fire. Or race each other. Or see if they can pump hard enough to overflow the box of the engine ahead of them when they're relaying. You've no control over your men."

The chief scowled and flushed deeply.

"Shall I kick them out?" he inquired. "Remember, please, they are volunteers and get no pay except what fun they have. Does the town want to raise more taxes so I can pay them and discipline them? Remember also that it takes thirty men to operate a fire engine and another thirty standing by to relieve them when they get tired. Quite a payroll."

There was a moment of silence and then Selectman John Houghton, who was somewhat younger than the others, spoke up.

"Steam," he said.

"That's all we've heard since that Cincinnati trip of yours," barked Perkins. "Steam, steam, steam."

"And that's all you will hear from me from now on," snapped Houghton. "The steam fire engine has ended all this sort of thing in Cincinnati. Two men run it. Never gets tired. Can pump all night."

"A newfangled contraption," grumbled Burrill.

"And while we're talking about contraptions," continued Houghton, "It's time this town had some sort of a fire alarm besides an old fool who is supposed to ring a church bell if he happens to be around. We need a fire-alarm telegraph and boxes here and there on street corners, so people can send an alarm and the firemen will know where the fire is instead of depending on seeing the smoke and running in that direction."

"Say, John Houghton, you must figure to bankrupt the town," shouted Mansfield. "And furthermore, if we break up the fire companies, each with 60 to 80 men, we'll lose votes. Twelve companies. Just multiply. What's your answer to that? Just you tell me."

"Steam," said Houghton.

He turned on his heel and marched off up Federal Street without another word.

"Revolutionary," rumbled Selectman Perkins, "Bankrupting."

"But it's got to come," said the chief. He swept a hand toward the ruined houses of Waterhill Street and the people moving their water-soaked furniture out to dry. "Fire fighting is a serious profession, not a series of picnics and dances and races and fights. And gentlemen, while we're on the subject, let's think about a water supply. Brooks and wells are not enough."

All this some of the men of Enterprise 11 and the Four Leaf Clover heard as they played their streams into the smoking ruins, but no more, for the Selectmen and the chief walked down the street, still talking, and one of them was scribbling on the back of an envelope.

3

The Age of Steam

THE GAY and tumultuous days of the huge, eighty-man volunteer fire company with its hand tub and fierce rivalries with other fire companies and its rum barrel attached to the apparatus did not end suddenly. Indeed, its most uproarious time was after the construction of two workable steam fire engines by two different mechanical engineers, in 1840.

In that year the New York insurance companies commissioned Paul Hodge to build a steamer. A year later the result of his planning and work was ready for a test in the city. It had a horizontal boiler, like a locomotive, and it was self-propelled; that is, it went to the fire under its own power without the need of horses or an uproarious gang of men to pull it.

The test was a great success, for the Hodge engine put a stream over the cupola of the New York City Hall. And yet it failed, for the vast army of volunteer firemen refused to co-operate with it in any way at fires. They saw to it that the steamer did not get the hose or the water supply it needed, and by a dozen sly and covert tricks they made this mechanical intruder look poor in its performance.

The insurance companies were not deceived in the least by the dismal fire record of their new steam fire engine, which they had bought and paid for to increase the efficiency of New York's fire-fighting force. They knew the volunteer firemen and all their peculiarities. But most importantly, the insurance companies knew they were absolutely obliged to depend on the volunteers and their beloved hand tubs to do 99 percent of the fire-fighting in the city.

So the Hodge engine was disposed of to power somebody's box factory.

The second steam fire engine was designed by Captain John Ericsson, a Swedish engineer of tremendous capability. The General Society of Mechanics and Tradesmen in New York offered a gold medal for the best design for a pumping engine operated by steam. Ericsson's engine won. It was Ericsson who, a little more than twenty years later, designed the USS *Monitor,* the iron warship with a revolving turret which fought the Confederate *Merrimac* to a standstill in Hampton Roads, Virginia.

Ericsson's design was never used; the City Council feared the big vote of the volunteer firemen and their families and friends. Here, again, the decision was based not on the merits of the apparatus, but wholly on grounds of policy. The volunteer firemen hated these machines and the volunteers must not be offended in any way.

No one in our present age of power-driven machines

should get the idea that the rejection of the steam fire engines was a serious matter. It was not. The hand-operated fire pump, perfected as it was in the mid-nineteenth century, could produce a stream sufficient to reach nearly everything a city had in that day. If the fire was a long one and the men got tired, there were plenty of spare men in the company to relieve anyone who wished to visit the brandy keg for refreshment.

The situation later became serious, not because the hand tubs were unable to furnish good, strong streams, but because wild fights developed between rival companies while fires were burning. The climax came in Cincinnati, Ohio, in the mid-nineteenth century, when the firemen were so intent on fighting each other that on several occasions the fires got away and threatened to become conflagrations.

The city authorities then realized something must be done, so they ordered a steam fire engine from the Miles Greenwood works of Latta Brothers in Cincinnati. At its first serious fire the Latta engine did excellent service until the volunteer firemen launched an attack upon it, cut its hose, threw rocks at it, and threatened to put it out of commission. A large group of citizens came to the rescue of the new steamer. A tremendous battle was fought right there at the scene of the fire. The volunteers were repulsed by the enraged citizens and the Latta engine stayed at work.

She pumped four streams, and to this engine went the chief credit for knocking down a tough fire. The episode marked the end of the hand tubs in Cincinnati and their enormous companies of turbulent men. The steamer needed only three men; the hose companies with a half-dozen men, laid the lines and manned the playpipes. The disgraceful uproars at fires, at picnics and barbecues and dances ended. Cincinnati became the first all-steam fire department in the United States.

In New York, in 1855, a big test was held in another attempt to introduce steam into the fire department. The Latta company sent its steamer *Miles Greenwood.* The New York volunteers sent their best hand tub, aptly named *Mankiller,* and with it threescore of the biggest and strongest men in all New York.

The hand tub *Mankiller* won the competition, beating the steamer with a stronger and longer stream. Yet the city officials could scarcely fail to observe that the *Mankiller's* crew were exhausted; they had worn themselves out at the brakes and lay about on the grass, resting. As for the steamer, it continued to pump with that rhythmic beat which is music to the ears of every old-timer who loves a reciprocating steam engine. The stoker was not tired; all he had to do was to toss in enough cannel coal to keep the boiler hot. The engineer was not tired; he watched his gauges and squirted oil into the oil cups now and then.

New York was not won over to steam that day, a fact which troubled the Latta men not at all. They drew the fire from the firebox, hitched up their horses, and headed for the freight yard. There they got their steamer onto a flatcar. In Boston the next day they demonstrated their engine, sold it to the city, and took the train for Cincinnati.

From then on, cities and towns purchased steam fire engines as fast as money became available. At sea, steamships were replacing the more romantic and majestic square-rigged sailing ships. On land, the steam railroads were putting the galloping steeds of the stagecoach lines out of business. And the conviviality and rivalry and spirit of the big volunteer fire companies gave way to the steam fire engine.

In this same era the sending of fire alarms by a tremendous ringing of church bells was replaced by the invention of the fire-alarm telegraph, devised by Dr. William Francis Channing of Boston in 1845. When a citizen or policeman pulled the hook in the fire alarm box, the number was transmitted to headquarters and from that point was sent to each fire station and to churches, whose bells tapped out the number of the box. This was so that the call men could leave their civilian jobs and report for fire duty at the box which had rung in. The first fire-alarm box was pulled in Boston in 1852. This alarm system is little changed to this day.

It took a few years to develop the steam fire engine into the piece of apparatus that was to be the backbone of American fire departments for nearly three quarters of a century. At first some steamers were self-propelled; that is, they ran over the streets by their own steam power. This method of locomotion never seemed to become acceptable to fire departments, mainly because the self-propelled steamers were too heavy and too slow. Yet it is to be noted that Boston and a few other cities had a couple of steam-propelled engines of later design that gave satisfactory service into the early twentieth century.

In the early days of the steamers, many were pulled to the fires by gangs of men, just as the old hand tubs had been pulled by men who loved to "run with the old machine." But the steamer was a different proposition from the lightly built hand tub. It was simply too heavy for any group of men to hustle along the streets to a fire unless they were seventy or eighty in number. To get that many men to report speedily to the fire station when the tapper hit proved to be very difficult. And a fire engine that does not start promptly for the fire is not much of an asset in the fire-fighting game.

It turned out, as the steamer gradually became the king of the fire department, that the best way to get this heavy machine to the fire speedily was with a team of three big horses. The horses were in stalls behind the apparatus and they were specially trained for their work. When the tapper hit for a box to which the engine responded, the man on watch at the desk threw a switch so that an electric mechanism flung open the door in the front of each stall and another switch activated a whip in the rear of each stall that gave the horse a smart flick over the rump.

Instantly the well-trained team came thundering out of the stalls and galloped past the apparatus to take their places under a complete rig of harness hanging from the ceiling. The driver pulled a cord, the harness dropped onto the backs of the horses, and the driver had no more to do than to snap the collars and he was ready to go. This was the famous "quick hitch." The driver sprang to his seat, took the reins, reached up to pull another cord, the front doors of the fire station swung open, and the apparatus rolled.

Old-timers who have been in a large fire station when the tapper hit feel sorry for young folks who never have had the opportunity to see a steamer's three horses come charging out to take their places under the quick hitch. At the same time out came two horses for the hose wagon, three for the ladder truck, two for the chemical engine, and one for the chief's buggy.

This whole uproar took place in no more than thirty seconds and then it was over, the fire station was silent, the apparatus was off down the street, bells clanging, firemen struggling into their rubber coats, small boys chasing along after them, and smoke from the steamer's stack leaving in the air the acrid tang of burning pine kindling.

The problem of how to have the steam fire engine arrive at the scene ready to start pumping was solved by some ingenious arrangements. While the steamer was in the station, its boiler was connected to a stationary boiler in the basement. Thus hot water at all times circulated through the steamer's boiler. On the steam connection, just above floor level, were snap valves, and it was the duty of the steamer's stoker to disconnect the pipes with one flip of the hand before the apparatus rolled.

To keep the boiler hot on the way to the fire, two bushels of pine kindling wood on a bed of excelsior were laid in the firebox. To light this was the duty of the stoker, who rode on the rear step in back of the boiler. Usually he had a metal holder into which were tightly packed a dozen or so wooden matches. The stoker struck this group of matches on a piece of sandpaper attached to the boiler and thrust this blazing torch into the excelsior in the firebox. He usually had his fire before the steamer was around the corner.

The story is told of the time when one of the firemen in the station wanted to light his pipe, so he helped himself to one of the matches in the holder at the rear of the steamer. The extraction of that one match spoiled the tightness of the group, but the stoker was unaware of it. Later in the day an alarm came in, the steamer rolled, the stoker grasped his match holder and drew back his hand in the motion of striking a light. The matches, loose, came out of the holder and scattered over the street. The three horses galloped along and the stoker was left with the problem of getting his excelsior and kindling going without his holder full of matches. He accomplished it after several attempts with matches from his pocket. Later on, in the fire station, his characterization of any fireman who would do such a thing as sneak a match out of his holder was a memorable oration of its kind.

When the steamer arrived at a fire, the stoker took a quick look before he decided what to do next. If it was a closet fire to be taken care of by a small line from the chemical company, he let his firebox full of kindling wood burn out, knowing that the chief would soon order his kit back to quarters.

But if the building was spouting like a tea kettle or flames were visible, he knew they had a working fire. Immediately he threw in some cannel coal from the boxes built into the platformlike step to the rear of the boiler. Cannel coal comes from England, usually in lumps and bar-like pieces. It is a quick-burning, hot fuel that was often used in fireplaces in the old days. This gave him quick steam.

With a coal fire going and black smoke drifting upward from the stack, the stoker turned to helping the driver get the big suction hose off the side of the steamer. One end they screwed onto the intake gate of the steamer; the other end they screwed onto the large gate of the hydrant. To handle the big suction hose, a hard suction, line it up, and screw it on was a good two-man job. Then they put the hydrant wrench to the nut at the top of the hydrant. This controls the valve. They walked the long-handled wrench around, the water came, and the steamer was ready to go to work.

While the steamer's men were struggling to hook up, the hose-wagon men threw off the butt ends of two lines of hose, coupled them to the outlets on the engine, and galloped toward the fire. The hose came off the reel, or, in a more modern wagon, it snaked out of the compartments on each side of the vehicle's body, and lay in the street in a line from the engine to the fire. Arriving in front of the burning building, the hosemen broke their dry lines; that is, they unscrewed a coupling in each hose line when they thought they had enough to reach the fire. Onto the ends they screwed their long brass nozzles and they they were ready to hit the blaze.

One of the men turned toward the steamer and bellowed "Water." The steamer's engineer eased open the throttle. The pistons moved, the fly wheel turned. He opened the throttle some more. The machinery gained speed. The lazy black smoke from the stack began to spurt upward in a straight column flecked with red-hot sparks as the cylinders exhausted their steam into the engine's flue.

The hose, lying flat and lifeless on the street, now rounded out, moved like a living thing to form long graceful curves, with water thinly spurting here and there from the couplings. As they saw the water coming through the hose, the men at the nozzle braced themselves. The stream began with a coughing spluttering sound, and the water was brown with pipe rust from the hydrant. Then the rust was gone, the spluttering was gone, and the stream gained strength until a straight edge could have been laid on it.

Three men hold the brass nozzle, for there is power here, power that must not be allowed to break loose. If the line should get away from these men, it would whip back and forth in the street like a great wild serpent and one blow from the brass nozzle on the end would break a leg as if it were a dry pine twig.

And the power of this stream from the steamer hits the fire with terrific force. It rips shingles from a pitched roof, tears off burning clapboards, hits the roaring flames and blackens the fire wherever it strikes. The steamer is now working at top speed as the stoker opens his fire door to toss in more cannel coal. The pistons flash up and down. The fly wheel is a blur with its spokes indistinguishable. The engine rocks up and down on its springs, and the black column of smoke from its stack stabs upward, higher than the nearby three-story building.

The horses, of course, were unhitched and led away before the engine went to work, for no animal could be expected to remain harnessed to such action and vigor without becoming unmanageable. And the shower of glowing coals falling all around would burn the hides of the horses, if they remained near. So they are tethered to a tree down the street.

If the fire was serious, a second alarm would be sent in, and perhaps a third or a fourth. If it was a major fire, usually the chief would call for ten blows, the general alarm that called in every piece of apparatus in the city. Then, if he was still fearful that the fire might get away, he would send word to headquarters to begin asking for aid from nearby communities. Many a conflagration has been averted by the timely arrival of out-of-town apparatus which helped confine the fire to the area in which it originated. At such a time, especially in the days of the wooden shingle roof, many of the out-of-town companies patrolled the area down wind, ready to extinguish immediately any fire started by burning brands.

At a big fire, where the steamers had to work at top capacity for a considerable time, the supply of cannel coal was used up. The stoker had to keep an eye on his coal supply and when he saw he was getting low whistle for coal. Every steamer had a whistle and every fire department had a coal wagon standing in readiness in one of the stations, loaded with gunny sacks of cannel coal. The chief would order the horses of one of the steamers to go back for the coal wagon, and when they galloped up to the fire scene they went to whichever engine was whistling for coal and the driver tossed off a couple of gunny sacks full. Then he would wait until another steamer whistled and move along to give that one its ration of fuel.

With many a man, one of the memories of childhood is hearing the extra alarms and seeing the glow of the fire in the night sky while his parents carefully explained that he was not old enough to go, but might be allowed to stay out of bed and at the window for a while if he would be sure to keep that blanket tightly around him. And in the distance he heard the whistle of a steamer calling for coal, then shortly another and another, and father would explain that the coal wagon was galloping from one to another of the engines to keep them supplied.

Back in bed, after parents had decided enough was enough, the boy could still hear the steamers whistling for coal, and finally he drifted off to sleep, making plans to go down there as soon as school was out on the morrow to have a look at the ruins. And when at last he did have a look at the fire scene after school next day or perhaps early in the morning while the firemen still had a couple of lines on the smoldering ruins, it was easy to tell which hydrants had been used, because a small pile of coal ashes lay in the street by each one.

In time the firemen discovered that the steam fire engine did have problems of its own. The prompt delivery of its pump-power at the fire required that the engine arrive at the scene with the water in its boiler hot. To accomplish this the two bushels of pine kindling were lighted as the machine passed through the front door of the engine house.

It was inevitable, of course, that glowing embers dropped through the grate and onto the street. If the wind was brisk these red-hot embers are blown into odd corners, under wooden stairs, or against fences, and soon there would be a new fire. Sometimes the chemical company was ordered to follow the steamer to watch for fires started by sparks from its grate.

This did not work out well. The glowing embers did not ignite wood against which they had blown until long after the fire engines had galloped down the street and were out of sight. A further disadvantage was that the chemical engine, a lighter and speedier piece than the steamer, was intended to be first at the fire in the hope that with its quick and smaller streams, the fire could be knocked down in its earlier stages. Every minute counts in fire fighting and if the chemical had to potter along behind the steamer, it forfeited the opportunity for a quick blow at a fire that might soon spread up a stairway or an elevator well or get into the partitions.

One windy day in March in a New England city the firemen responded to a box at the far end of the harbor front. Along their route were several marshy areas and in the early spring dry grass is not hard to find anywhere. Fortunately this fire turned out to be a false alarm, for on the way back to quarters the chemical engine and the hose wagon had to attend to four grass fires set by the steamer's wind-blown embers on its way to the box.

This writer can recall a coal-yard fire, a general alarm, where two steamers were hooked up to the gates of one hydrant, and working with a will. From each stack a straight column of black smoke flecked with red sparks towered upward.

Across the sidewalk from these splendid engines was a small house with a wooden shingle roof. It was showered with embers of glowing cannel coal from the stacks of the steamers and it was not long before the shingles were ablaze.

The proximity of the steamers made this problem easy of solution. A fifty-foot length of hose was connected to an outlet on one of the engines, the roof of the house was drenched, and from then on, every ten minutes, the stoker picked up the nozzle, opened it part way, and gave the roof another shower.

In the early part of the twentieth century appeared the first signs that the steamer, too, might go the way of the hand tub. The automobile had been invented and early models were chugging around, so it was natural for efforts to be made to adapt it to use in fire fighting.

It was not long before the manufacturers produced motor fire apparatus with a pump driven by the same gasoline engine that propelled the vehicle to the fire. A gear shift enabled the operator to change the drive shaft when he arrived at the fire so that the power was delivered to the pump instead of to the rear wheels.

In principle this was an excellent idea and it is the principle upon which every modern pumping engine works today. But with the idea of a motor fire pump, as with every new idea, it took time for engineering to catch up. The early motor pumps were unreliable. Gasoline engines were not rugged enough to carry the burden of two- or three-hour pumping assignment at a big fire. They broke down, the gear shift often failed to work, and the parts of the rotary pump sometimes fractured under stress.

The transition was gradual. Many departments were unwilling to turn their backs on the steamer, the backbone of firefighting for over half a century. Yet they realized the advantage of motor-driven apparatus to get to the fire, especially when distances required a run that tired out the horses. It is recorded that in the year 1906 or thereabouts, when Lynn sent a steamer to the neighboring town of Nahant, which is reached by a mile-long road built over the coastal sand dunes, one of the horses dropped dead upon reaching the fire. The run from the Lynn fire station to the road, then that mile, and the further distances over Nahant streets were too much for the animal.

Many fire departments reached a compromise between the age of steam and the age of the gasoline motor. They built tractors on the front of their steamers, so that the engine traveled to the fire with its motor and then pumped with steam.

There were several types of tractors, the most interesting being the American & British, which had a powerful motor that ran an electric generator. There were two electric motors, one for each front wheel, and each wheel operated independently. The rear wheels were the ones that were originally on the steamer; big tubber-tired wagon wheels.

The driver of one of these tractors had to be quite a man. To begin with, to spin the enormous steering wheel took powerful arms and shoulders. Sometimes a rubber tire from one of the big front wheels would work loose as the steamer banged along over the cobblestones. Then the tire would come off, go bounding over the pavement, and perhaps end up by staving in a plate-glass window or bowling over a pedestrian.

The biggest problem for the driver was the situation that resulted when the electric motor driving one wheel failed and the other continued to function. Had Hercules been at the wheel he could not have prevented the steamer, under such circumstances, from going off at an odd angle.

Upon one such occasion the steamer fetched up on a lawn. The perspiring driver, as he dismounted, was heard to give fervent thanks in language very much his own, that the old girl had chosen to misbehave opposite a stretch of green grass rather than on the main street, where plate-glass windows fronted every building.

As the years passed, the engineering of the motor pumps improved, so that they became more reliable, faster, and in every way fine apparatus. No new steamers were purchased. The old ones wore out. Their aged boiler tubes sprang leaks while working hard at large fires, and the water poured down into the firebox. They were not repaired; always a new motor pump was purchased as a replacement.

The writer recalls an evening in 1928 when last he had the privilege of seeing a steamer hard at work. It was the last steamer in the department, a fine La France with an American & British tractor. All the other steamers had been replaced by motor pumps.

The fire was in a tannery, the general had been sounded, and every piece of apparatus was at work. The steamer, being first-alarm apparatus, had a hydrant near the fire, with three lines off her, and she was doing wonderful work.

She was whistling for coal. The stoker had thrown his last lump into the fire box, but the arrangements for the coal wagon must have been allowed to go a little slack now that everything else was motor pumps. No coal wagon appeared.

Gradually the beat of the magnificent machine slowed. The three strong, straight streams that three crews of hosemen were directing into the fiercely blazing structure began to weaken. They were no longer straight. They weakened and arched until they barely reached the fire.

The engine's beat slowed even more as the steam pressure dropped; she was just about turning over. The chief arrived, red-faced and shouting. Then, while the chief was halfway through his speech, the coal truck, an old hose wagon, came upon the scene with sacks of cannel coal.

The stoker seized the first sack to be tossed off the wagon, flung open his fire door, and began tossing chunks of coal into his dying fire. Here was a wonderful example of the quick action of cannel coal; the steam pressure mounted, the engine's beat quickened.

The three streams of water directed at the fire had become pitiful dribbles. Now they increased and straightened, and soon the three crews again had powerful streams tearing into the heart of the fire.

And that is how this writer likes to leave his memory of the steam fire engine; power, motion, rhythmic and cadenced beat, a straight column of red-flecked smoke, the glow as the stoker opened his fire door to toss in more coal, and those three long, straight streams striking into the very heart of a general-alarm fire.

4

Hand-Tub and Steamer Stories

ONE CAN never tell by looking at a fire engine what adventures it may have had. But all of them except the very newest have witnessed exciting events. There are breathless moments when an engine is part of the first-alarm apparatus at a big one and the men struggle to lay a line and have their hose burn in the street before the water comes. There are times when a fire starts to spread and the firemen move the engine out of the way just as its paint is blistering and the front seat cushions are burning. There are long pumping assignments from midnight to dawn with the temperature ten below and hydrant, hose, and street ice-coated, and the operator freezes his hands and some greenhorn is brought in to run the engine.

Occasionally the part that a piece of apparatus plays in a fast-moving drama is recorded somewhere. More frequently firemen tell the story over the years when they get together to talk about old times and the hot work their engines have done. Sometimes the story is told by buffs or sparks, who somehow managed to be present when a tough fire got out of hand.

This writer recollects a cold winter evening in 1925 when he was a student at a school for young men in Hanover, New Hampshire. Word reached town that a serious fire was in progress at White River Junction, Vermont, five miles south of us in the Connecticut River Valley. We could see the red in the sky, and the news was that the Junction House, a large old wooden railroad hotel, was burning.

The few student automobiles were soon in motion, and all of the very numerous taxi fleet of old Cadillacs were on their way down there, carrying students by the dozens. This was a tremendous fire for a little North Country town; indeed it would have been a major blaze for a large city. I recall the resources summoned up to meet it.

White River's motor pump was at work, and the motor pumps from West Lebanon, the town on the other side of the river, and from Lebanon, five miles to the east. Today, with better roads and better apparatus, engines from much more distant points would be present.

However, more fire engines that night would have done no good, for the water mains of White River Junction were small, incapable of supplying more than the three motor pumps already at work. But more water was needed to contain this dangerous fire in the middle of the closely built little railroad town. And they managed to get more water.

From the town of West Hartford, in Vermont, a few miles up the White River Valley, came a strange fire engine. It had a powerful gasoline motor, probably taken from a large truck or purchased from one of the agricultural machinery companies. This the townspeople had mounted on a frame of their own construction that rolled on four automobile wheels.

They had bought a good pump from one of the manufacturers, and the village mechanics had connected it to the motor. The result was a good engine—cheap. In case of fire, the first farmer to arrive at the engine house with his truck loaded on the hose, took this piece of apparatus in tow, and started for the fire. Everyone else, notified of the location of the fire by the number blasted out on the town's bull whistle, went streaming along after the pump.

These men arrived at White River Junction and at once learned that the hydrants could not take another engine without creating a water shortage that would rob the already existing streams of their strength. Immediately they manhandled their pump down a bank to the ice on the White River, chopped a hole, dropped their suction pipe, stretched their lines to the fire, and went to work. In a country fire department with a strong whistle to blow the alarm, it is not unusual to have a crew of twenty to man an engine. So the hose was hustled to the Junction House in jig time and two more heavy streams joined the fight.

White River Junction, in addition to its quite new motor pump, had the steamer that had done duty over the years prior to the arrival of their modern engine. The town authorities, foreseeing some such emergency, kept their steamer in good condition, ready for action with a towing rig attached and an understanding with a townsman who owned a caterpillar tractor that he would get the engine to the fire.

Someone in authority must have provided the fire department with a list of the wells in town, for on this night the tractor towed the steamer to a nearby well, the men got a line to the Junction House, and the stoker fired her up. When that well was pumped dry, the hose was disconnected and the tractorman hooked up and snatched the steamer to the next well. More hose was laid, and the steamer went to work again.

When I saw this machine at work in some citizen's back yard, I was told it was pumping at its fourth well and they knew just where they were going when this one was dry. The engine was a joy to watch as her crew pushed her to the limit to get their strong stream through the long line of hose to join the fight.

The old hotel was, of course, a total wreck, a heap of charred timbers with pieces of unburned wooden wall left at points where the water had been the strongest. The important fact was that the huge fire had been confined to the building of origin and had not swept through the rest of the town.

This result the Vermonters achieved by using every last resource they possessed—three motor fire engines, the West Hartford machine working from a hole in the ice, the steamer, probably too heavy for the river ice, but supplied from the wells of the neighborhood. And it was a close call, with nothing to spare.

In 1872, on that dreadful November evening when the fire at Boston's Summer and Kingston streets got wholly out of hand, the chief soon realized he needed any out-of-town help he could get. The fire was traveling; one after another of the mercantile buildings along Summer and Chauncey and Bedford streets became involved. The situation was wholly beyond Boston's twenty-one engine companies.

Desperately the chief gave orders to telegraph for help. This was before the day of the telephone, but the chattering keys of the telegraph, talking in Morse code, spread the word of the conflagration consuming Boston and appealed for help.

Some nearby places got the word by messenger; Cambridge, the Charlestown Navy Yard, Brookline, Newton, and their apparatus were soon on the way. The telegraph, then widely used for short-distance messages, reached cities such as Lynn, Salem, Waltham, Lawrence, and Beverly. Some came with their horses, some came on railroad flatcars.

In these early stages of Boston's appeal for outside aid, there appeared an example of the true fireman's spirit. In Wakefield, twelve miles distant, some of the men of a hand-tub company still active although a steamer had been acquired, gathered at their engine house to talk about the red glow in the southern sky. Plainly a terrible fire was in progress somewhere nearby, perhaps in the neighboring town of Melrose or possibly beyond, in Malden.

All a real fireman needs to know is that there is a fire and he wants to be there, at once. The rest of the company were quickly rounded up, the doors of the engine house swung open, and off went the Wakefield hand tub and its hose reel to help put out this fire that reddened a whole quadrant of the night sky. They reached Melrose, only to find that the fire was not there. The Wakefield men, not running now, strained at their drag ropes as they hauled their engine into Malden, the town beyond.

The fire was not in Malden, but they knew now, from the word on many lips, that this was a conflagration in the very vitals of Boston. Onward they went toward the ever-brightening sky, very tired now, yet as completely determined to be in this tremendous fight as they had been when they swung their piece out of their engine house back in their home town.

The Wakefield hand tub reached Boston and took a position on Broad Street. There its good stream helped check the northward spread of the conflagration. The men worked at the brakes of the old machine until they were ready to drop. Then men in the crowd stepped forward to relieve them, and the stream continued to punch into the blazing building, along with the streams of nearly fifty other out-of-town engines, mostly steam, on this side of the fire.

Victory was the reward, for nearly all of State Street was saved. For these exhausted volunteer firemen there was no reward equal to victory. And this is true of all firemen, everywhere.

The busy wires carried Boston's desperate plea for help to Worcester and Providence and Fall River and New Bedford and even to Norwich and New Haven in Connecticut and many other cities and towns. In each the reply was the same; engine and hose wagon to the freight yard and up a plank ramp to a flatcar. A message to the railroad brought a locomotive backing down from the roundhouse to couple on, a caboose on the rear end, and away they went.

These short trains roaring over the iron toward Boston were obliged to stop for nothing, for the dispatchers telegraphed orders ahead for everything else to get onto the nearest side track and leave the main line clear. Long before they reached Boston the firemen, huddled against the cold near their apparatus on the flatcars, could see by the red glow in the sky that plenty of hard work awaited them.

When the telegram reached Portsmouth, New Hampshire,

the chief gave orders to hustle Kearsarge No. 3 and her hose wagon down to the freight yard. Word spread quickly around town and by the time the apparatus was aboard the flatcar and the locomotive was coupled on, there were eighty-eight firemen and volunteers ready to go along.

At top speed they rolled down the Eastern Railroad. They whipped through Newburyport with the engineer working his whistle in a long series of deep-throated blasts. They clattered through Ipswich and Beverly, slowed for Salem Tunnel, and picked up speed as the engineer worked steam through the great castellated granite station.

In Lynn people turned to watch them as they rattled over the many grade crossings and they cheered as they saw this shining steam fire engine rushing into the battle to save Boston, only ten miles away. Across the Lynn marshes, through Revere and Chelsea, and into the North Station yards rolled the Portsmouth train.

No sooner was the train at a standstill than the plank ramps were snatched off the flatcar by the crew and the apparatus was manhandled down the slope and onto the ground. A messenger from the Boston chief was on hand urging them to hurry. Another critical point in the great fire had been reached, said the messenger; the fire was moving inexorably down the east side of Washington Street, the Transcript Building was afire. One jump across Milk Street and the flames would devour the historic Old South Church, a landmark since colonial times.

The Portsmouth men needed only this word to spring into action. All eighty-eight of them, and a dozen or so men in the railroad yards, laid hold of the drag ropes and started their engine for the fire. In front of the Old South Church a crowd was gathered. They knew this was a point of crisis. If the fire crossed Milk Street and involved the Old South, not only would they lose this church beloved by generations of Bostonians, but the fire could then progress down Washington Street to consume even more of the very heart of their city.

Streams were playing on the Old South, yet they lacked strength to reach farther than the eaves of the roof. Burning brands had blown through the slats in the belfry of the tower and smoke was rolling out.

The flickering red glow in the belfry seemed to be increasing. Grimly men watched this fire high above them, beyond the reach of the feeble streams. The church seemed doomed.

Then, north on Washington Street there was yelling and shouting. The crowd parted, and in the red light of the conflagration they saw a hundred men and boys on the dead run with the shining boiler of Kearsarge No. 3 at the end of their drag ropes. Smoke was coming from the stack of the steamer as her stoker, riding the rear step, worked on his fire to build up a head of steam. A great cheer went up from the crowd as the Portsmouth engine rolled up to a hydrant.

Furiously the stoker heaved cannel coal into his firebox. Men unloosed the big black suction hose from the side of the steamer and connected to the hydrant. Other men snaked the smaller, two-and-a-half-inch hose from the wagon and horsed it up to a position near the Old South. The long brass nozzle was screwed on.

"Water," bellowed the captain, and the Kearsarge engine, a new Amoskeag not long from the factory at Manchester, began to turn over.

The water spluttered feebly from the nozzle, coughing out air pockets and hydrant rust; the stream arched onto the ground and then splashed as far as the lower wall of the church. The steamer's beat increased, the smoke from her stack began to stab straight up, spark flecked.

The stream picked up as the engine's speed increased, straightened out, pointed upward, climbed the side of the steeple. The four men on the nozzle braced themselves to hold it steady.

In the street, every man held his breath and was almost on tiptoe watching that stream climb the tower, wondering whether it could possibly reach the fire in the belfry. Then the stream, strong and powerful, struck the wooden slats. The water cascaded into the belfry. The glow ceased; the smoke thickened and then gradually became thinner.

From the street arose a tremendous cheer, and men slapped one another on the back. Many went over to have a closer look at this engine whose power had given victory when defeat seemed a certainty. The mayor of Portsmouth, who had taken the ride with his men, stood proudly beside Kearsarge's boiler answering any questions the Bostonians cared to ask.

The Old South Church was saved. Men climbed up inside the tower to the belfry to make sure no lingering sparks remained. The Kearsarge's men continued to drive her hard. Now her powerful stream was turned on a blazing building on the other side of Milk Street to knock down all fire there and remove any further danger of spreading. Here was victory at this point of the fire. A good stop, as firemen phrase it; a heartening moment on a very discouraging night.

As a footnote to this epic of the never-ending battle against fire, everyone interested in the game will be glad to know that Kearsarge No. 3 still lives. For years she was in James Filluel's fire-engine museum in South Manchester, New

Hampshire. After his death, she passed into the hands of another man who loves her.

Many believe, with Rudyard Kipling, that a machine can have a personality, be it ship or locomotive or fire engine. That a noble mechanism such as the Kearsarge engine should fetch up in a junk heap is a thought revolting to any man who knows of its long career and its moments of greatness and believes that it, too, has an aspect of immortality.

The big day for Engine 1 of Lynn, Massachusetts, turned out to be Palm Sunday in the year 1908. Lynn is a seacoast city; the next town south of it is Revere; beyond is Chelsea and then Boston itself. Engine 1, a fine Metropolitan La France steamer, and its hose wagon were stationed on Commercial Street in the western part of the city.

The firemen had cooked and eaten their Sunday dinner, and were washing the dishes, when a friend of many cribbage games dropped in. Usually a placid individual, he seemed very much excited this day.

"Want to play a little cribbage?" queried the driver of the hose wagon.

"You won't finish any cribbage game today," snapped the man. "You won't have time. You're going to get a run."

"How do you know we're going to get a run?" queried the captain. "If you saw a fire on your way down here, why didn't you pull the box, the way a good citizen is supposed to, instead of wandering in here and sitting down and telling us we're going to get a run. What a man."

"Cap'n, keep your shirt on. Tell you how I know. I just came in from Boston on the trolley car. Came through Chelsea, and they've got a fire over there that's just plumb out of hand. Started in a junk yard and with this wind that's blowing today, it was ahead of them from the beginning."

Every fireman in the house was gathered around him now. "Smoke and burning brands blowing across the main street there so the motorman of our trolley car could hardly see where he was going. Bet it was the last car through Chelsea. I saw the Everett steamer come wheeling in and one from Malden and one from Boston. They'll need more, much more. Just get on your rubber coats and sit on the kit, boys. You're going to roll."

The man was right. It was only a few minutes before the desk telephone rang sharply and the man on watch jumped to answer.

"Engine 1 and the hose wagon to Chelsea," he barked as he replaced the receiver.

The steamer's three horses and the hose wagon's two came galloping out of their stalls to take their places under the harness hanging from the ceiling. The drivers snapped the collars and girths and out they went. They were not through West Lynn before the drivers realized that no horses could gallop all the way to Chelsea. They slowed to a trot and by the time they were halfway across the marshes, the horses were walking and all the men except the drivers had dismounted and were plodding along behind.

Upon arrival in Chelsea, Engine 1 was ordered to Bellingham Hill, an area not yet involved, but directly downwind and very much threatened by the onward-marching conflagration. The driver of the steamer unhitched his horses and led them to a place of safety. The hose wagon laid two lines, the engineer hooked up to the hydrant, and the stoker worked away at his fire to build up a head of steam. When the engineer saw a sufficient reading on his steam gauge, he cracked his throttle and the engine began to turn over with smooth steady power.

On one side of them was a Chelsea company working in an atmosphere of smoke and burning brands; on the other side a company from Cambridge. Nearby was a small cemetery that the chief hoped would provide a fire break.

Lynn's engine had two strong streams. So did the Chelsea steamer. So did Cambridge. But it was not enough water. Roaring and crackling through block upon block of closely built wooden dwellings, many of them three-story tenement houses, the conflagration swept down on a broad front with unbelievable speed and heat.

Directly in front of Engine 1 a three-decker began to smoke. The window glass, expanding with the heat, cracked with a noise like the popping of hundreds of corks and dropped out. Fire entered, curtains flamed, then entire rooms caught and soon the whole building was burning. The blaze rolled and swirled across the narrow space to the next structure and it was the same story over again; popping glass, rooms in flames, and in a short time the building was a great torch.

The Lynn men stood up to the fire; they reversed their helmets to protect their faces and poked their two straight, heavy streams into the heart of the flames. Their steamer was working to the very limit, giving her men every pound of her pumping capacity. They were very good streams, good enough to knock down any ordinary house fire, but not enough for a fire like this.

The Chelsea company shut down and backed out. So did

the Cambridge company. The boys of Engine 1 knew they could not stay and yet they were not willing to yield.

One of the men shouted in the captain's ear.

"Chelsea and Cambridge companies have pulled out, Cap'n."

"Hell, they ain't firemen," shouted the captain, watching his two straight streams hitting into the fiery inferno of a three-story tenement house. "They should be working on a ribbon counter."

He cocked his ear to the roaring, drumming beat of his steamer, a sound that fills the heart of any true fireman. Yet, where he stood the roar and crackle of the flames was louder. He knew his two streams were being turned to steam before they could have any real effect on this building. The captain knew he must surrender.

"Back out, boys," he shouted. "Tell the steamer to shut down."

But he had traded one punch too many with his adversary. The great red wall of fire, backed by the crucible heat of half a city burning, rolled over them and over their steamer. The engineer did not have time to shut down the pump.

They ran for their lives. They made it with very little to spare. Behind them lay their hose, whipping wildly, yet still playing water into the burning area. Behind them their engine still pumped, even though engulfed by flames.

Rubber coats scorched, faces blistered, eyes red with smoke, hands scarred by red-hot embers, they raced out of the fire area, at last reaching a spot beyond the hellish blast, where they might pause, rest, and breath clear, cool air.

The captain sat on a curbstone, tears running down his cheeks.

"Listen, boys. Hear our steamer. She's still pumping. Hasn't she got a nice beat."

The Chelsea fire rolled on. After the Lynn men had rested and been given coffee and doughnuts at a Salvation Army post, they turned to and helped other engine companies and lent a hand with the people who were fleeing with whatever possessions they had snatched from their burning homes.

Most of the refugees had armfuls of clothing, blankets, and pillows; some carried chairs or dragged mattresses, while a few less practical ones struggled along with whatever had seemed most precious at the moment of flight. One man had a heavy black ormolu clock, a little boy clutched his toy fire engine to his breast, and a sobbing woman had her canary cage, but the bird lay lifeless at the bottom.

None of the fire companies now attempted to stand in front of the roaring holocaust. Realizing it was impossible to check the fire with a frontal attack, they fought along the sides, trying to keep its path as narrow as could be. In this part of the fight, Lynn's Engine 3, a neat little two horse Amoskeag steamer, did excellent work on the north flank, keeping the fire from working to windward toward Revere.

The conflagration burned down to Chelsea Creek, a salt-water river one hundred feet wide, beyond which lay East Boston. There, dozens of Boston's steamers concentrated and with them were deck guns capable of taking in three engine lines and sending out a really massive stream of water of tremendous reach and power.

Across the creek the battle raged as the heat and the millions of glowing embers beat upon the Maverick Oil Works and the wooden tenements of East Boston. Here the battle was won. East Boston was not involved.

After midnight, when the Chelsea fire was at last under control, Engine 1's men went back over the hot pavements to look for their steamer. They found it in the street, scorched and blackened, its metal parts warped and twisted by the intense heat, its wooden wheels and seat and coal boxes burned off. The rubber suction hoses were wholly consumed, except for their spiral metal stiffening. The hose they had laid in their attempt to stand in front of the fire was gone. Here and there they found the brass couplings, but of the hose itself nothing remained; even the ashes had been whirled away in the inferno of heat.

Through the rest of the night Engine 1's men helped other companies wet down the glowing ruins along the edge of the fire. With the dawn they went for the steamer's three horses and at last found them in an open field on the outskirts of town.

When they started back to Lynn, ten sad and weary firemen rode a hose wagon empty of all its hose. Behind them, tethered to the rear of the hose wagon, trotted the steamer's three big gray horses.

When they reached their station, they backed in, unhitched their horses and led them to their stalls, and loaded a new suit of hose into their wagon. Now they were ready for the next alarm, for even without their steamer they could lay a hydrant line and their area had sixty pounds of pressure in the water mains.

The captain, once the hose was in place in the wagon, threw back his shoulders, stepped to the telephone, and turned the crank.

"Engine 1 back in service," he said crisply. He hesitated a moment. "By the way, tell the chief we're running with just the hose wagon. Our steamer needs some work done on it."

5

The Great Chicago Fire

THE GREAT Chicago Fire was a blaze that would make hell itself look like a two bagger. Seldom, if ever, has there been such a ferocious and tremendous fire on the face of old Mother Earth. The statistics give the outlines of the appalling disaster.

The fire traveled four and a half miles from its origin on the South Side of the city to the northern limits at Lake Michigan and the prairie, where it ended only because there was nothing more to burn. The area destroyed was over three and a half square miles, and 17,450 buildings were consumed, including many important public buildings, hotels, theaters, railroad stations, and business establishments. There were two hundred and fifty known dead and it was estimated that the number of dead would have reached five hundred if those whose bodies were totally consumed by the terrific heat could have been counted.

The loss was $200,000,000, and 98,500 people were left homeless. Sixty American insurance companies went bankrupt because of the losses on their policies on Chicago property. Criminals were on the loose and looting was general. Two thousand special police, six companies of militia, and four companies of Regular Army troops from General Philip Sheridan's command were required to restore order. Seven persons were shot while looting or trying to spread the fire. Several women gave birth to babies in public parks and on sidewalks, unattended by any skilled person, and some of them died on the spot.

Some people died as they ran from the fire, killed by taking into their lungs the hot blast of the superheated gale. After the fire their bodies could not be located. They were wholly consumed and the ashes blown away, becoming part of the vast smoke cloud that rolled over the city.

Granite exploded, sandstone crumbled, marble became lime, metal and glass melted, wood became ashes and blew away. The homeless encamped in parks and on the prairie; lost children wandered about, wailing. Some refugees had a few belongings they carried with them. Most had no more than a blanket or a coat or nothing at all and counted themselves fortunate to be alive, for few there were who had not seen some fellow human perish before their eyes.

The story of this terrible disaster begins with the O'Leary family on De Koven Street on Chicago's South Side. Their tenants, the McLaughlins, were having a glorious party on that Sunday evening, October 8, 1871, and they needed more milk for a tremendous drink called a Tom and Jerry. Mrs. O'Leary, to please these good tenants, took a milk pail and a kerosene lamp and went out to the barn in the middle of the evening to milk a cow that had already been milked a few hours before.

Kate O'Leary set the lamp on the floor, placed the milk pail under the udder, and went to work on the cow, which approved not at all of the irregularity in the schedule of milking. Cows are ordinarily contented and peaceful beasts, but there are limits. This one, annoyed, kicked backward, hit the lamp, and tipped it over. The oil ran out onto the straw on the floor. The lamp ignited the spilled oil and the straw and the hay in the loft.

Kate O'Leary threw her few cupfuls of milk at the fire and ran from the blazing interior, screeching. The family threw buckets of water, but the fire was beyond such measures. Daniel Sullivan, an Irishman with a wooden leg, went into this inferno to untie the five O'Leary cows, but his efforts terminated when the end of his wooden leg became firmly wedged in a space between two of the floor boards.

Realizing his desperate situation, Sullivan quickly unstrapped the wooden leg, reached over to a heifer tied near him, put one arm around the creature's neck, and with his other hand undid the knot. He came out of the barn at a terrific clip, hanging onto the frightened heifer's neck, but his wooden leg remained behind and became one of the earliest victims of the great Chicago Fire.

The cantankerous O'Leary cow became one of the most famous animals in the entire course of history, easily eclipsing the Trojan Horse or Jumbo. The unthinking millions, leaving out numerous important factors, took the view that this immense and staggering disaster was caused by this creature. She soon became famed in song and story. She had poems written about her, one being entitled "The Cow That

Burned Chicago," composed in lame and far-fetched doggerel. This thing was put to music for the vaudeville stage.

Various aspects of the O'Leary affair were debated acridly and at great length. The people who sought to analyze every detail of what took place in the little O'Leary barn that windy October night genuinely believed they were debating the cause of a fire that laid in ruins so much of a great city.

They were but amusing themselves. Really it mattered nothing, absolutely nothing, whether the fire started because the cow kicked over the lamp or whether it was boys smoking secretly in a haymow or a rat gnawing on the head of a match. What made a barn fire become a disaster rarely equaled and never exceeded actually had nothing to do with what particular event caused the hay and straw in that small barn to catch fire and burn furiously. The real causes of Chicago's disaster were much deeper.

To begin with this city in less than forty years had grown from a little outpost on the prairie to the metropolis of the West with a population of over three hundred thousand people. Railroad terminals, hotels, grain elevators, wharves, factories, and business buildings had all been built in this prairie town in less than four decades. And the dwellings of these hundreds of thousands had all been built in this short space of time.

The word was always "hurry." Building laws had not been developed. Wooden cottages stood close together, sidewalks were of wood instead of brick, shingles of wood rather than slate. The city was a vast and crowded jumble of wooden structures, with new ones being slapped together every week to make homes for the train loads of Irish, German, British, and Italian immigrants arriving from East Coast ports.

At such a clip had Chicago hurried to build homes and so crowded in were the wooden dwellings that an inspector from the great Lloyd's of London insurance organization was aghast when he examined the city. Upon receipt of his report, the Home Office ordered that no more insurance be written on Chicago property and that outstanding policies be canceled whenever possible. This was but a short time before the evening Mrs. O'Leary tried to get a little extra milk from her immortal cow.

The hastily and closely built structures of the fast-growing metropolis of the prairies was a factor, but only one. A general-alarm fire the night before burned over sixteen acres of buildings and came very near getting entirely away. After a desperate battle the department halted it, but at a price. The price was the temporary loss of two steamers damaged by falling walls and the complete exhaustion of nearly every man in the fire department.

Also, the summer and autumn of 1871 was a time of intense and unrelieved drought. Not since early July had there been any substantial rainfall. The prairies were dry, and forest fires in Wisconsin and Minnesota were frequent and serious. The vast acres of wooden residential Chicago were tinder dry.

Another factor was a delayed alarm. The fire-alarm box was pulled very early in the fire, but the box did not transmit and the alarm was not received at headquarters.

So the fire raged in closely built De Koven Street, relentlessly moving from one house to the next until the night sky was an angry red. Engine 6's crew saw the fire and rolled, even though no alarm had been received.

The red glow in the sky, the flames, and the sparks were

soon visible from fire-department headquarters. Although no alarm from a street box had been received, it was realized that a serious fire was in progress and headquarters sent out help. But the man on watch in the tower had judged very poorly as to the location of the fire, and the engines were sent to an alarm box a mile away from the fire on De Koven Street. This was forty minutes after a citizen had pulled the box nearest the O'Leary fire.

However, the firemen sent out by headquarters were not long in spotting the fierce blaze at De Koven Street, which was spreading rapidly to other streets of closely built little wooden houses. They promptly galloped over and joined the embattled crew of Engine 6. But forty minutes had been lost.

When the chief arrived he sent for all the rest of the city's fifteen working engine companies. He should have had seventeen, but two had been disabled at the near conflagration of the day previous. Telegraph calls for aid began to go out to all cities in that part of the state.

Another factor this night of October 8 was a high wind from the south that carried the flames from one house to another. Sparks and burning brands were carried aloft by this half gale to fall blocks away on bone-dry wooden shingle roofs and stairs and porches. The result of such a storm of fire was inevitable; new fires sprang up everywhere downwind from the main blaze.

So here in Chicago on this evening was a very devil's brew. Closely built wooden houses and wooden sidewalks. A drought that had dried wooden shingles and everything else to a tinder-like state. A fire department worn out by the terrific battle of the previous day and short two engines. A delayed alarm, always a fireman's nightmare. A high wind.

This combination resulted in the great Chicago Fire. Mrs. O'Leary's cow was a picturesque item that appealed to the multitude. Had anything else ignited the inflammable little barn set close to other similar structures, the result would have been the same.

Any fireman following an account such as this hopes to find the story of some good stops; points where the department managed to check the blaze. For a while it was thought that a stop might be made in the area where the fire started, so that it might be confined to a few blocks. This they had accomplished with the fire the night before.

With the whole department at work, it seemed as if they might surround and hold this one. Then came word that St. Paul's Roman Catholic Church, several blocks distant, had caught fire from burning brands. Steamers were taken from the main fire to fight this new one, and yet the church fire spread to nearby factories and soon was entirely out of hand.

The original fire, because these engines were withdrawn from the battle, then became uncontrollable. Soon the two fires became one, roaring down on the miles of the city that lay in its path. The sixteen acres burned over the previous night did not stop it. The Chicago River did not stop it.

The wind impaired the usefulness of the streams of the engines, for the solid column of water was broken up into spray before it reached the point at which it was aimed. At this stage of the fire another characteristic of a conflagration became an adverse factor; the heat generated by large numbers of burning buildings.

Firemen cannot stand before such heat. Streams of water directed at the front of such a fire by firemen in a sheltered spot become steam and do not really reach the burning materials. The firemen can do no more than fight at the sides of a conflagration, hoping to keep it from spreading laterally.

There must have been some good stops at Chicago, else the fire would have spread south and west and east. It is regettable we do not have accounts of the valiant battles fought at the sides and to windward instead of the surplus of horror stories we do have.

So the Chicago Fire, now of such tremendous volume and heat as to be unstoppable, roared through the city, the high wind from the southwest pushing it. Vast areas of wooden dwellings were swallowed up, and the residents fled with what little they could carry. Some who carried on their backs a mattress or a bundle of blankets or clothing found that their burdens were afire from the storm of sparks and burning brands. So they cast their flaming possessions into the gutters and hurried on, and many found that holes had been burned in their coats when at last they reached a place of safety.

The engineer in charge of the gas works, hoping to reduce the hazard, turned valves that permitted gas to escape from the great gasometers into the sewers. This did not save the gas works. When the leaping flames reached it the gas remaining in the tanks exploded with an earth-shaking roar, demolishing the entire plant and many surrounding buildings.

The gas that had been let into the sewers did not explode. Not then. It leaked out of various manholes along the sewer line, was ignited by burning brands, and provided numerous smaller but dangerous explosions that helped spread the fire.

The court house, standing by itself in a ten-acre tract, was thought to be safe, although in the path of the conflagration.

Yet when subjected to the intense heat of the onrushing fire, the windows cracked and dropped out, the wooden interior caught fire, and soon the building was a roaring furnace, even though it had massive stone walls and a slate roof.

The water works, which took water from Lake Michigan, was reduced to a ruin. Its great pumps stopped and the firemen were faced with failure of water in the hydrant system.

In the downtown area the fire attacked the hotels, office buildings, factories, and railroad stations. The stone and brick and steel in these important structures did not check the fire. The buildings were not truly fireproof and were full of inflammable contents. They were wiped out just as surely as were the wooden shanties in the DeKoven Street area.

Yet we do have one account of a stop made to leeward, right in the path of the fire. And this stop was made not by a fire company, but by a stout-hearted home owner.

This man had a small house in the North Division, in the outskirts, a house he had been years in building with his savings. As for fire insurance, he had none. Today it would be unthinkable to be without fire insurance, but in 1871 the idea of insurance was not fully established.

This citizen saw the fire coming. He had plenty of news that it was destroying all in its path, but he went right to work while the fire was distant. He raked up all the dry leaves around his house and carried them away. Then he tore down the picket fences, ripped up the board sidewalks, and got rid of the lumber. He removed his front and rear door steps and took the boards away.

He had a ladder and he spread wet blankets and rugs over his roof. Working valiantly at the pump at the well in his yard he kept putting water on the blankets and rugs as the heat of the approaching conflagration began to be felt. Now burning brands were falling fast as the fire neared his house. With his bucket he doused them wherever they fell and he continued to monkey up his ladder to put water on his roof.

Finally fire was all around him, but he kept on working in the fierce heat. Nearby houses caught fire, burned fiercely, and fell into glowing ruins. At the hottest point in his battle it seemed as if he must lose after all, for his well ran dry. But he had one more resource. In his cellar he had a barrel of cider laid by for winter. He filled his bucket with cider, time after time, and continued to douse any part of the house that commenced to burn.

When the cider barrel was empty, the fires in the nearby houses were dying down, the storm of sparks was over, the heat had diminished. He had won. Only one other building in the district survived; a stone mansion with a slate roof in a wealthier street some blocks away.

This man, who won so astonishing a victory, was helped a little by two favorable factors. The fire, when it reached his area, was feeding on smaller buildings, and therefore the heat probably was less intense. Also, the houses in his area were more widely spaced, so the problem of radiated heat and flames reaching from one building to another was somewhat less.

Even so, the factors that gave the margin of success were his courage, his foresight in preparing his fight while the fire was distant, and his determination in keeping on with the fight even when he was reduced to using cider instead of water. One official said afterward that it would have made a difference if a number of citizens of Chicago had put up a real fight. If they had taken active steps to stop the fire from spreading by burning brands, if they had done some wetting, if they had done what little each one could, the disaster might have been less.

At last the greatest fire North America had ever seen completed its four-and-a-half-mile march through the metropolis of the West and flickered out at the very edges of the city where there was nothing to burn. After it was over, the very next day, the drought which had been one factor in the disaster was broken. It began to rain, on the hordes of homeless huddled in parks and on the open prairie with no shelter; some with blankets or coats, some without.

These wet, cold, wretched people, without homes or possessions, were in desperate need of help. Help came. That first night schools and churches and business buildings and private homes were opened to give shelter to the refugees. The Regular Army troops of General Sheridan's command did their part in sheltering refugees in tents and feeding them Army rations.

The telegraph sent the news of the plight of 150,000 homeless over the wires to every community in North America and cables carried the word overseas. The situation of these thousands of destitute touched the hearts of people everywhere, and the generous, open-hearted relief sent to Chicago was the one inspiring feature of this massive misfortune.

Contributions of money ran into the millions. Bales and boxes and barrels of clothing were an almost universal contribution, for nearly everyone had some such article that could be spared. Every town in the country, it seemed, made a collection and sent at least one barrel of clothing, and some of them dozens. The railroads carried all relief supplies free of freight charges.

From United States Army Quartermaster depots came 10,000 blankets, 4000 each of shirts and drawers and pairs of stockings, 1500 pairs of shoes, and 195 tents. From the stores of the British Army in Quebec came a gift of 6270 blankets.

Interesting are some of the things that people here and there across the country had on hand that they could spare and that they knew would help stricken Chicago.

Leavenworth, Kansas, a frontier town not far from Dodge City, sent five bales of buffalo robes. Lacon, Illinois, gave sixty cords of firewood. Welch & Griffith of Boston shipped three hundred hand saws for carpenters to use in rebuilding and to saw up firewood. Massillon, Ohio, consigned twenty-five carloads of coal. Allegheny City and Braddocks Field, both in Pennsylvania, sent twenty-six carloads of coal between them.

Mr. A. J. Cohen of Shickshinny, Pennsylvania, shipped ten carloads of coal. Several woolen mills in the East sent quantities of blankets, and from Leeds in England arrived nineteen bales of blankets. All these items were very welcome, with the bitter prairie winter coming on.

There were many donations of food, such as apples and potatoes by the barrel, hams, one thousand loaves of bread from one bakery, and canned goods from many sources. From Illinois, Iowa, and Missouri some of the food donations were in carload lots.

Here and there in the pages of the *Report of Chicago Relief and Aid Society* are listed gifts of a more individual and imaginative nature. One Boston firm sent a large tent. An-

New York Public Library

One of the earliest fire engines (1733), with power supplied by foot treadle. Note the bucket brigade bringing water to pour into the "tub." *Below:* This 1854 picture shows hand tubs at the peak of their development. Note the hydrant and hose reel and three different models of hand-operated engines.

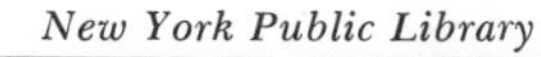

New York Public Library

Lynn Public Library

Silver Grey, she's cream all over,
And no machine can wash her over,
So pump her hard and keep her clean,
Ten, Ten away. Call come where it may
Her ropes will fill and down the hill
We'll rattle the Silver Grey.

Silver Grey No. 10, built by S. & E. Thayer, Boston, 1844. Cost $700. Completely rebuilt by Hunneman & Co. 1856. Photo taken in 1860's after rebuilding.

"Faithful and Fearless."

FOURTH ANNUAL BALL,

OF THE

RELIANCE ENGINE CO.,

Number One, of Salem.

The pleasure of your company, is respectfully solicited, at

HAMILTON HALL, SALEM,

On Friday, (Christmas Eve,) Dec. 24th, 1858.

Music, Brown & Boardman's Quadrille Band.

Tickets, $1.50, including Supper for Ladies.

COMMITTEE OF ARRANGEMENTS:

Capt. A. J. Tibbetts, T. H. Williamson, J. B. Osborn,
D. B Hood, F. F. Wallis, H. L. Hill,
Nath'l Soley, J. W. Averill, G. F. Tibbetts,
W. M. Hill, D. B. Lord, Jr, J. H. Kehew,
C. H. Dalton.

Hutchinson, Pr., Salem.

Printed invitation to a fireman's ball, 1858.

The two pictures on this page were taken at Firemen's Musters. *Right:* Pipemen of Torrent No. 1 of Bath, Maine. *Below:* Protection No. 1 of Newbury, Massachusetts.

Harold S. Walker Collection

This engine in New York is really working steam. The horses have been unhitched and led away as usual.

Harold S. Walker Collection

Two steamers at work. The fire is beyond the fence in a wharf occupancy.

Harold S. Walker Collection

Harold S. Walker Collection

Engine No. 38 of Boston, a self-propelled machine that went to the fire under steam power. *Below:* a Metropolitan steam fire engine with an American La France tractor.

Harold S. Walker Collection

Harold S. Walker Collection

Engine No. 14 of Milwaukee, Wisconsin, taking water from a slip along with other steam fire engines. The picture was taken after 1899.

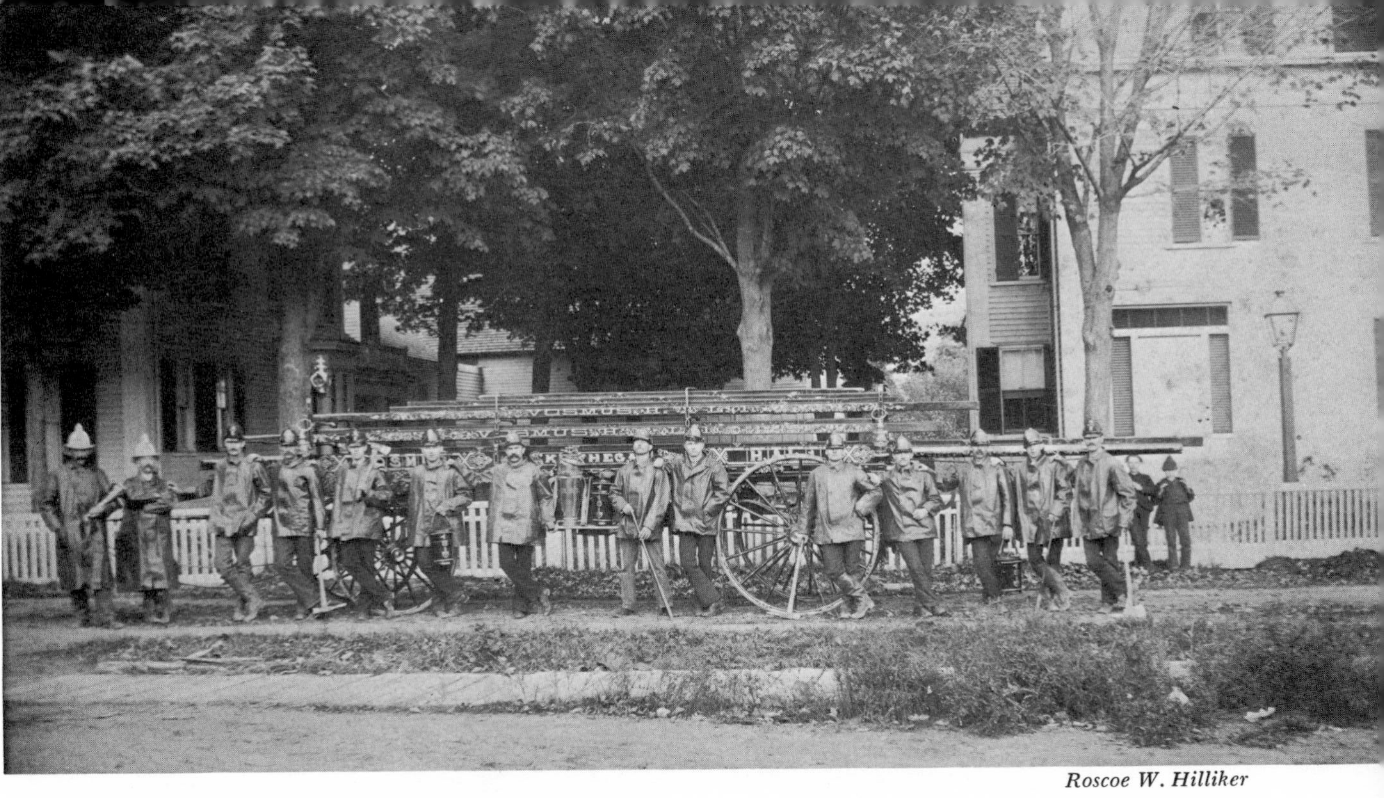

Roscoe W. Hilliker

Early ladder truck, Skowhegan, Maine, probably hand drawn. Note the officers with white helmets, and the correct postures for firemen who are being photographed.

Roscoe W. Hilliker

A chief's buggy. The horse looks as if he could get the chief to the fire ahead of the apparatus. *Below:* A ladder truck with a three-horse team, an eighty-five-foot aerial ladder, and a tiller man to steer the rear wheels around corners.

Roscoe W. Hilliker

Roscoe W. Hilliker

The Metropolitan steam fire engine of the early twentieth century was a powerful, big-city, heavy-duty piece of fire apparatus. *Below:* The Button engine, made by the Button Engine Company of Waterford, New York, was unusual because its steam cylinders and pumps were horizontal.

Lynn Public Library

Right: This steamer in Omaha, Nebraska, has been pumping a long time at a big fire in sub-zero weather. *Below:* This chemical engine with a three-horse team carried two vertical sixty-gallon tanks and worked from a downtown station that also contained steamer, hose wagon, and ladder truck.

Harold S. Walker Collection

Roscoe W. Hilliker

Benjamin Ellis

Boston fire apparatus arriving in the freight yard in Salem, June 1914.

Roscoe W. Hilliker

A horse-drawn hose wagon. The shield hanging from the wagon behind the horses kept mud from dirtying the shining paint of the wagon. *Below:* A chemical engine with two fifty-gallon tanks. A unit like this would be alone in a fire station on a city's outskirts.

Roscoe W. Hilliker

Benjamin Ellis and Joseph E. Scanlon, Jr.

Getting a heavy steamer through snow was a difficult problem in the days before motor plows went to work early in a storm. This steamer in Boston, normally drawn by three horses, needed the extra power of two more to get through snow-clogged streets.

Seven steam fire engines pumping from one cistern at a fire in the French Quarter of New Orleans. Steel flues on the smokestacks are raised to give a better draft to the fires under the boilers.

Harold S. Walker Collection

Roscoe W. Hilliker

A beautiful Amoskeag steamer, its horses, and its full-time crew. The men standing on the ground rode the hose wagon to the fire.

other Boston group, the "Prisoners and attaches of the Charlestown State Prison," demonstrated their feeling for the victims of fate by sending a money contribution of $617.32.

From Baltimore came seven cases of bedding and clothing given by the Hebrew Ladies Sewing Society of that town. It is interesting to note this early example of the ready response of Jewish people to the needs of the unfortunate.

Perhaps with the disastrous results of the overturning of Mrs. O'Leary's lamp very much in mind, the Cleveland Non-Explosive Lamp Company gave two hundred and seventy lamps and twenty-four oil cans. Parenthetically it may be observed that it required many years of development to perfect lamps that could safely burn the kerosene of that day. Part of the reason lay in the fact that there was no market then, as there is today, for gasoline. The kerosene sold for use in lamps was much more volatile than that sold today because much less of the more volatile gasoline had been distilled from the petroleum after it came from the oil wells. Thus there was considerable danger of explosion in the lamps.

Looking forward to the time when these refugees would again have homes, the Peekskill Mutual Stove Company gave twenty-five cook stoves and other companies gave a number of bedsteads, tables, bureaus, and crates of dishes.

Two of the gifts show how deeply the misfortunes of Chicago's homeless touched the hearts of people across the country. Listed is the gift of one quilt by Mrs. Lynch of Fair View Post Office in Pennsylvania. Doubtless this was a patchwork quilt with some very interesting squares of cloth in it, put together over a long period of time by the good lady. With great inner satisfaction she delivered this work, her pride and joy, to those who were making up the shipment to Chicago.

This, she knew, would cheer some poor soul in the dreary winter just ahead.

In California, those who were making up a relief shipment greeted a small boy who appeared in their depot carrying a little cloth bag. This he explained, contained his marbles, and he wished to add them to the load going to Chicago, because he had been thinking of all the boys in that city who now were without anything to play with. This bag of marbles would help one of them, said the boy, who, the record tells us, was named E. B. Lewis.

Lessons there were from the Chicago Fire; some that were emphatic reiterations of old principles, some that were newer.

What happens when a fire in one structure gets out of hand in a large area of lightly built wooden houses had been learned in Boston two hundred years earlier. These Chicago people were too absorbed in building the fastest growing city in the world to study the history of Boston or any other town or even to consult their own common sense. So the small crowded-in wooden dwellings by the hundred burned so furiously that their very ashes, swirled aloft by the half gale, were carried away in the red-flecked clouds of smoke and nothing was left to show that these little homes had ever existed.

Board sidewalks, wooden shingles, and above all, a delayed alarm, are all prescriptions for disaster; lessons often given and often forgotten. But in the fury of Chicago's disaster came a clearer realization of what is not fireproof. Walls of brick or stone are not enough, if the building has a wooden interior and unprotected window openings. Naked steel beams can bend like melting candles. Radiated heat can ignite a courthouse standing in a ten-acre park if there is exposed woodwork on a mansard roof or if windows lack metal-covered shutters.

The fate of the buildings in downtown Chicago, the very best buildings of that day, laid the foundations of the science of fireproof engineering. From this fiery laboratory came the experience and the data with which to plan future construction.

6

The Night Boston Needed Help

In november 1872, not much more than a year after the conflagration that swept through Chicago, it was Boston's turn to suffer a major disaster. There were similarities. The Boston fire was a conflagration of the first magnitude, wholly out of control; and one of the reasons it got away was a delay in sending in the alarm.

There also were striking differences. In Boston there was no wind, whereas on the night of the Chicago Fire, a half gale was blowing. Boston's fire started in a mercantile district of substantial stone and brick buildings. The fire in Chicago started in a district which not unjustly was termed a "shanty town."

In Chicago drought was a factor. Boston had no such problem. In Chicago, miles of little homes were wiped out; but in Boston, it was largely business occupancies that were destroyed, and only a few roomers and families were affected.

Chicago's fire department had enough water to supply the steamers had they arrived promptly. In Boston a major cause of the disaster was a lack of water. A six-inch main on Summer Street, laid when the district was residential, was soon overtaxed by the second- and third-alarm apparatus. Many of the buildings were five stories in height, and the weak streams were not effective even when directed no higher than the third floor.

One further and very important difference can be mentioned. At no time had it been possible to gain control of the hurricane of fire that charged four and a half miles through Chicago. In Boston there were several victorious battles that resulted in saving important sections of the city's business district.

The story of the Boston fire, as is always the case with a bad one, presents several features of an unusually unfortunate nature. On November 9, 1872, a disease called epizootic afflicted most of the horses in the Boston area. This ailment, a type of influenza, was rarely fatal, but it put the horses down in their stalls, utterly unable to do any work whatsoever.

Business firms managed to do some trucking by obtaining oxen. The streetcars, then horse drawn, carried on a very meager and limited service with the few animals that had escaped the disease. The Board of Engineers of the Boston Fire Department held a meeting on October 26 to decide upon measures to meet the situation brought about by the horse disease.

First, the strength of each company was doubled by the enlistment of volunteers. Second, the use of horses was temporarily discontinued with the thought that the animals should be given the opportunity to achieve full recovery. Third, drag ropes were furnished each engine house so the greatly increased personnel could pull the apparatus by hand. Fourth, and most important, the number of engines responding on the first alarm to each box was drastically reduced.

Box 52, the one which hit for the great fire, was normally listed for a response of six steamers. On Summer Street, near the corner of Kingston Street, were situated a large number of four- and five-story buildings occupied by the dry-goods trade, and therefore containing quick-burning materials. It had been realized that the six-inch water main in Summer Street was quite incapable of supplying enough water for a fire involving even one of these tall buildings. So six steamers was the normal first-alarm response to provide the strength and power to bring hose lines to the fire from other streets.

But when the meeting of October 26 had ended, Box 52 was listed for a response of one steamer on the first alarm. Here were sown the seeds of disaster. What these good men were thinking of when they did such a thing is impossible to imagine. They finished their deliberations by taking Engine 16 and Engine 18 out of service entirely, and then they did one wise thing—they notified police to sound the second alarm immediately if the fire was above the third story. They could better have asked the police to sound the second alarm if the officer on patrol could see any fire whatever showing.

At seven o'clock on the evening of November 9, 1872, Boston's twenty-one steamers, seven ladder companies, and eleven detached hose companies were all in quarters. The horses lay ill in the stalls. The regular firemen and the extra volunteers lounged about, reading the newspapers, playing cards, and swapping yarns. All was peaceful and quiet, and all remained peaceful and quiet much longer than it should have.

Few were on the streets in the mercantile district. It was Saturday evening. The work week was over. The only busy streets were those in the theater district. A lone pedestrian saw fire in the five-story building at Summer and Kingston streets. Then others saw it.

They stared at the light mounting story by story as the fire climbed from the basement up the pine-sheathed elevator shaft.

The box, famous Box 52, was not pulled. To pull the box it was necessary to go to the place where the key was kept. In those days the authorities saw to it that the key to each box was in a safe place, in the custody of someone nearby who would not let it go unless he was convinced there really was a fire. No pedestrian went for the key.

When the fire had climbed the elevator shaft to the fifth floor, it began to spread through the dry goods. It mushroomed. In the top of the building was a hoop-skirt factory, and the flames roared through the laces and crinolines and whale-bone frames with wild fury. But still no one pulled the box. Over in Charlestown, where the Boston & Maine Railroad crosses the river on the Prison Point drawbridge, the bridge tenders opened the draw to let a ship pass through. They noticed the glowing smoke cloud in downtown Boston. The clock on the wall said 7:08, yet no alarm had reached fire headquarters.

Although no one had hunted up the key to the box, a number of people were doing what was quaintly known in that day as "hallooing fire" as they watched the fire involve the entire building. A police officer, attracted by the shouting and the glare of the fire, came on a dead run from a neighboring street. He had a key and he used it at once to open the box and send the alarm. Then, following orders, he immediately sent in a second alarm.

So the famous alarm from Box 52 hit at 7:24 P.M. And, as the box hit, the operator at fire-alarm headquarters could see the fire from his window, a fire that had been burning for nearly half an hour. He had his orders. To this box, which before the epizootic called for a response of six steamers, he sent one steamer. Firemen from another steamer, No. 10, saw the fire from their quarters and rolled without orders. On the second alarm two more steamers responded, and when the third alarm came in at 7:34 P.M., all in-town engines swung into action. All of them arrived drawn by gangs of men and boys. On a short run, their running time was nearly as good as that of the horses, but on longer runs a gang of men could come nowhere near the time a team of horses could make.

As soon as the chief arrived, he ordered the general alarm (three twelves), which summoned every piece of apparatus in the City of Boston. The building was a living furnace, but only Engine 7 was in action. Other steamers were arriving handled by gangs of exhausted men and boys.

Engine 4 took the hydrant at Kingston and Summer, across the sidewalk from the burning building. Here, although the heat was terrific, these firemen stuck to their post with all the courage that firemen have always shown. Theirs was a strategic spot, where with very short lines they were able to cut hard into the very center of the flames.

Here, for the first time that night, occurred the phenomenon that was to plague the firemen constantly; exploding granite. This noble building material is the result of a mixture of several kinds of stone that flowed together in a molten state in the fierce volcanic heat of the days when the world was young. These different kinds of stone expand at different rates under heat, and the stone which expands at the lowest temperature exerts tremendous pressure on the other stone in the mixture.

So granite flies apart, explodes, under intense heat. This fact Engine 4's men discovered the hard way when the granite in the upper stories began to shower them with fragments. They stood their ground. Then a piece of granite, weighing a quarter ton, split off, hurtled down, and broke Engine 4's suction hose. At this point the captain decided it was time to shut down and move to another hydrant.

From the very first, the situation deteriorated rapidly. The mansard roofs on the other side of Summer Street began to smoke in the fierce heat. Here Boston learned that a mansard roof is a treacherous construction in case of fire. The dormer windows are encased in a considerable amount of wooden trim, and there were wooden cornices. High on the fourth or fifth story, they receive all the heat from a nearby burning structure, the flame and the glowing brands.

This day it was found that mansard roofs communicate fire readily. The fact had been suggested by a study of the Chicago fire in its later stages, when the conflagration had swept through large areas of wooden dwellings and finally attacked the business section. After the Boston disaster, the chief was severely criticized for not having taken steps to counter the danger of many mansard roofs in the downtown section.

The critics did not state what measures the chief should have taken to meet the known danger of mansard roof construction. Today, a water tower, a pipe on the tip of an aerial ladder, or a stream from a deck gun would be used. These, however, were not developed as early as 1872. Even if the chief had been fortunate enough to have such apparatus, he did not have the water pressure necessary to make it effective.

A good stream from a hand line on the street would reach a mansard roof. The chief did not have good streams. They did not reach. As more steamers arrived, took hydrants, and went to work, the six-inch main gave less and less water. As firemen phrase it, the engines were "running away from their water." When the firemen took a second line off a steamer that was pumping one good line, they found they had two weak lines.

They raised ladders, hoping to fight the fire now in the upper stories of several buildings by carrying lines up and hitting it at close quarters. Some of the ladders caught fire and had to be taken down. Where men did manage to get to upper floors, either by stairways or over ladders, fierce heat forced them to back out.

The fire crossed Summer Street in a number of places. At the corner of Otis Street a fierce heart-breaking struggle was lost because there was not enough water. The buildings caught fire at the top in the mansard roofs, windows broke in the intense heat, the top stories commenced to burn, and the fire worked on down through the buildings.

Not long after eight o'clock the chief realized that this was more than a big fire; it was a conflagration. He was helpless to check the spread of fire from the top of one building to another. Although there had been little wind when the fire broke out, there was wind now, the fierce drafts set up by the vast heat of the fire itself. These drafts carried flames from one building to another, and he had no streams with reach enough to protect any exposure in upper stories. Water from the streams splashed off the lower stories and ran deep in the gutters while upper stories burned furiously.

The chief gave what orders he could. Some spare steamers were sent for, dragged by men to the scene, and put to work. He dispatched a messenger to the Western Union office on State Street to request aid from every community within fifty miles of Boston. The clattering telegraph was busy carrying the news that Boston was burning, and the messages went much farther than fifty miles.

Inexorably the roaring conflagration marched through the mercantile district as the firemen fought valiantly, but without any success in preventing its progress toward Boston Harbor. Street after street of buildings melted before the flames, and owners with hired wagons loaded merchandise from stores and warehouses and hurried off to the Common with what little they were able to save. Walls crashed to the ground; great clouds of smoke and burning brands rose from the hellish heat and drifted toward the harbor; the heavens glowed an angry red. People as far as Worcester could see in the sky the signs of a great city being destroyed.

While the business heart of the city was being burned out, street by street, there was a lot going on in fire departments all the way from Portland, Maine, to New Haven, Connecticut.

Apparatus from nearby came over the road. Cambridge was the first to arrive, and they had three steamers at work before the fight was over. Other nearby towns got in soon after, Charlestown, Chelsea, Brookline and Somerville, Newton and Lynn, Salem and Waltham. The Navy Yard sent two steamers and the Watertown Arsenal, one.

A hand tub from Wakefield came thirteen miles over the road. In towns farther away, the railroads provided locomotives, flatcars, and coaches, and the dispatchers cleared the tracks. From Providence came three steamers and hose reels; from Norwich, Connecticut, two; from New Haven, one; and from Worcester, two. Down from Portsmouth, New Hampshire, on a flying special train, came the famous steamer Kearsarge No., 3 with hose wagon, forty-five men, and the mayor aboard.

Up in Manchester, New Hampshire, the news that came over the telegraph wires created great excitement. One of the city's steamers and its hose wagon headed immediately for the railroad yards. In Manchester was the Amoskeag Company, the maker of fine steam fire engines over the years. They had developed a self-propelled steamer, an eight-ton affair that could go to a fire under its own steam power, using a rig in principle like a steam locomotive.

This machine, named *Vesuvius,* was the Amoskeag Company's contribution to the Boston fire, and it, too, was hauled to the railroad yards and put aboard a flatcar. Then three passenger coaches were hooked on and two hundred citizens went along to help, including seventy regular members of the Manchester Fire Department. Of all these two hundred people aboard the train, only the regular crews of the city steamer and its hose wagon were obliged to go to Boston.

As to the journey of the Amoskeag self-propelled to the Boston fire, let there be a word of warning here. There exists in print a story purporting to be told by an old character, a lifelong Amoskeag employee, who claimed that he rode to the

Boston fire *over the road* on this extraordinary piece of fire apparatus. The story is well told; it recounts in detail the journey of this eight-ton monster with iron-tired wheels and a top speed of fifteen miles an hour over the roads that existed in 1872.

One only slightly acquainted with machinery may wonder how this steamer ever got up some of the hills on the route and what brakes they had to hold it on the downhill slopes. The yarn tells how they stopped at Nashua and Lowell for coal and water, so no one can accuse the narrator of saying the engine went to Boston on the coal she carried on the rear platform.

At the end, the old narrator tells what the *Vesuvius* engine did to the great Boston fire after this sixty-mile trip over the road. His story sounds like hitting a brush fire with an engine line.

This yarn is spun from moonbeams. We have investigated it fully. However, the engine did fight at the Boston fire after it was unloaded from its flatcar, contributing powerful streams to help in the successful battle to keep the fire from crossing to the west side of Washington Street.

In the story of the Boston fire, dismal episodes occur aplenty, such as the delayed alarm, the reduction of the number of engines answering the first alarm and the second, the weakness of water pressure on Summer Street that prevented the firemen from making a good fight of it at the beginning. Yet there are bright pages; the response from out of town of forty steamers and their hose wagons and four hand engines gives us today a bit of inspiration.

Another bright page, a corollary of the splendid help other cities gave Boston in its time of trouble, is a series of heroic and successful stands made by the firemen at key points. These successes would not have been possible without the extra help that came into Boston over the highways and by railroad. The arrival of out-of-town engines resulted in an array of apparatus triple the size of Boston's department.

Here is a marked contrast with the Chicago Fire. In Boston, control was gained at four key positions. In Chicago, there is no record of a good stop, of control at a point that saved a district from destruction.

The first of these battles was along the west side of Washington Street. The east side was all aflame and the issue was whether the fire would jump the street, as it had so many others, and burn its way up to Tremont Street. The Common would be a bar to further progress along part of Tremont Street, but north of Park Street it could have jumped the street and burned up to the State House and on into Beacon Hill.

An epic fight was waged along Washington Street. Employees and citizens swarmed to the defense of the Hovey Store and other structures. Wet blankets were hung on wooden cornices and dormer windows, and they were kept wet by men with dippers and buckets who sloshed water from windows and from positions on roofs.

In this area the water supply was better, out-of-town engines were in the fight, and the streams were much stronger. These straighter and more powerful streams played on the burning buildings on the east side; and, as one witness wrote, the streams hit "with enough effect to take some of the wickedness out of the fire." So along the line of Washington Street there was victory, and the fire got no farther on that side of the conflagration.

In a previous chapter we have described the critical situation on Washington Street, at the corner of Milk Street, when the steamer Kearsarge No. 3 from Portsmouth saved the Old South Church. This stop saved not only the church but the whole north side of Milk Street.

On Devonshire Street, at the corner of Milk, another critical phase was the defense of the new post office, a building not yet fully completed. Streams from the engines were concentrated on the new building, and the granite never got hot enough to explode. Water was plentiful here. The firemen hit the fire hard and prevented it from working northward at this point.

Yet farther down Milk Street, not more than a hundred yards distant, the fire did jump the street, and was working along Congress Street toward State Street, probably the most important thoroughfare in Boston. At the corner of Congress and State was the Merchants Exchange, and the fire swept furiously into this large stone building with its interior of wood. If the Merchants Exchange was fully involved, the fire would be of such volume, heat, and intensity that there would be no hope of saving the rest of State Street and the streets lying to the north of it. This area to the north included Faneuil Hall, the market district, the stores and shops on the way to the North Station, and then the station itself, the bridges, the Charlestown Navy Yard, and the whole area of Charlestown.

Here on Sunday morning was fought the most crucial battle of all. And here, at last, was concentrated a force bigger than any ever seen before. State Street was full of steam fire engines working from hydrants or from reservoirs and cisterns or taking lines from other steamers at a distance and relaying the water to the fire. As the steamers worked, a dark pall of coal smoke from their stacks hung over the district. Over forty engines were assembled at this point and the atmosphere hummed and throbbed as every engineer pushed his pump as hard as it would go.

Here at last, the firemen were inside the building, working with strong streams and plenty of them. It was a desperate toe-to-toe fight. They hit the fire wherever it entered the building and knocked it down. When the battle was won, the Merchants Exchange was a partly burned, waterlogged wreck.

Little did anyone care. It was victory. At this point the fire was stopped dead in its tracks. Word was flashed across the city that the conflagration had been halted, and all over town people sighed with relief and could smile again.

It was Sunday noon when at last the fire was confined. The mayor requested that the out-of-town firemen remain for a while to guard against any new outbreak. Well it was that they did so, for that night a gas explosion started a serious fire at Washington and Winter Streets. For a while it looked as if this one, too, might get away, but with out-of-town help it was quelled.

Little remains to be told and that little is usually the aftermath of any conflagration disaster—wetting down ruins, of course, and examination of safes after the ashes have cooled to see if the contents survived. In Boston, as in Chicago, there were fierce disputes over the effectiveness of blowing up buildings to stop the sweep of the fire.

The gunpowder argument had raged during the fire, with a great deal of harsh language. It raged after the fire, the opponents charging that the explosion merely blew out the windows of stone buildings, making easier the entry of fire, and reduced wooden buildings to a heap of kindling that burned faster.

As is always the case, the chief was criticized for various shortcomings in his handling of the fire. He survived the criticisms. One allegation made against him is interesting. It was said he was weak on general planning and showed a lack of experience. One is inclined to ask how one lays general plans to meet a fire that sweeps unchecked to the waterfront, and where one gains experience to deal with such a disaster as the Boston fire.

The firemen fought valiantly and in the best tradition of the American fire-fighter. Thirteen of them were killed in this fire and nine of the dead were out-of-town men. There was no hanging back. The men gave their work all they had; they risked injury and even death, and to them what they were doing was more than mere labor. It was a sacred duty.

7

Disaster at San Francisco

IN THE YEAR 1906 San Francisco was a vigorous young giant of a city with four hundred thousand people and energy and optimism and faith in a wonderful future. It had everything: the blessing of a excellent climate, the riches of the abundant countryside or hinterland of which it was the economic capital, a magnificent harbor that sheltered the shipping of the Oriental trade and vessels from Europe, South America, and the East Coast of the United States.

The goldfields, farms, ranches, and forests all brought their business to San Francisco, and railroads and ships made this city their terminus. Three quarters of a century earlier the easygoing Spaniards had a tiny community here. Soon the more vigorous Russians and Americans were looking into this lovely bay with appraising eyes. The prize fell to the Americans as a result of a war with a Mexican government that had failed to understand the power of the westward movement of the people of the United States.

In 1849, a moment in time after this land became American, gold was discovered not far from San Francisco. An explosive happening, this, from a historical viewpoint. The discovery, valuable as it was, served only as an opener to the economic opportunities of vast, fruitful California. San Francisco was the center, the focus of this growth, this unlocking of the treasures of the Pacific Coast.

Hurry was the watchword of the day, of every day from the surge of the Forty-Niners who came by ship and overland until that eighteenth of April in 1906. California hurried to get things done and it got things done. In fifty-seven years the sleepy hamlet on the shores of this far western bay became one of the great cities of the world. It had skyscrapers, important banks, big newspapers, the famous cable cars, a magnificent opera house, theaters, and beautiful parks. And it had the homes of four hundred thousand people; wooden, crowded, built in a hurry.

San Francisco had an excellent fire department with thirty-eight steamers, and ladder trucks and chemical engines in proportion. The department had to be good, for in this city of crowded frame buildings, fires threatened quickly and decisively. The San Francisco Fire Department knocked down many a fire that could have got away if handled by a less powerful and competent force.

But the Board of Fire Underwriters was not at ease with this little town that had become a great city in so short a time. The vast areas of tall, crowded wooden buildings worried them. In 1905 the Board had this to say: "San Francisco has violated all underwriting traditions and precedents by not burning up; that it has not done so is due largely to the vigilance of the fire department, which cannot be relied upon indefinitely to stave off the inevitable." In another report the insurance inspectors had stated that San Francisco was the most hazardous city in the United States.

But San Francisco had its superb fire department to fight its battles. Then, in a few early morning minutes on April 18, 1906, one of its weapons was struck from the hand of this fire department. The water mains were broken in a thousand places by an earthquake. Thus deprived, the department had to go forth to battle.

The earthquake was a violent one. The interior of old Mother Earth had been disturbed that year like the insides of an old lady who has eaten too much lobster. Vesuvius, the Italian volcano, had put on a fearful performance. An earthquake in the Caucasus region of Russia and Turkey had caused severe damage.

Extending through California is a fault, a section of the earth's crust where subterranean readjustment can occur. There had been such a disturbance in California in 1868. It was this fault that again heaved uneasily on April 18, 1906. Chimneys toppled, masonry crumbled and dropped from buildings into the streets, wooden buildings collapsed in odd and contorted ways. Modern steel and concrete buildings standing on good, solid ground suffered little, even though tall enough to be classed as skyscrapers today. But the areas of San Francisco built on "made" land—marshes filled with ashes, mud flats covered with rubbish and gravel—damage and loss of life was heavy.

The damage from the earthquake, although of major severity, was not the real disaster. It was fire that ruined San

Francisco, just as fire had struck grievous and devastating blows at Chicago and Boston. Had San Francisco been obliged to sustain only the damage from the earthquake, recovery would have been no great problem.

We have already noted that every general conflagration results from a combination of adverse factors. It was so with Chicago and with Boston. So it was with San Francisco. First, the lamps and stoves that toppled over in the earthquake, the electric wires that short-circuited, the stove pipes and chimneys that fractured started a least thirty separate fires.

Then, second, the fire-alarm system was wrecked by the shocks of the quake, so that when citizens tried to send alarms, no signal sounded in headquarters.

Third, when the fire department was summoned by messenger or responded because they could see one of the fires, they found they had little or no water. The water mains were broken in so many places that few of the city's hydrants were functioning. This is the factor that really spelled defeat for the San Francisco Fire Department. The men fought valiantly with the water from the few hydrants that were working, from cisterns, and from the harbor. It was not enough —not nearly enough—and the fires merged into a general conflagration.

Fourth, and of tremendous importance, was the inflammable character of large areas of crowded wooden buildings, many of them of a height unknown in most cities. The Fire Underwriters had made very pessimistic remarks about the character of the city's buildings. With other factors so unfavorable, the day of reckoning for the city was at hand.

And as if all this was not enough, the able chief who had directed so many victorious battles against bad fires was mortally wounded by collapsing masonry. He was taken from his bedroom after the quake had toppled a brick chimney down into the building and upon him. He was conveyed to a hospital, where he died before the ashes of his beloved city were cool.

One acquainted with the fire-fighting game has no difficulty in understanding how this combination of adverse circumstances developed very early into a general conflagration, an enormous, sweeping fire that was entirely out of hand. The various fires that had started were nearly all soon out of control. They progressed through block after block of crowded wooden buildings, merged, and become one. Then as one wide front, they marched inexorably toward the business section.

At this stage the fire had the characteristics always observable in a conflagration. Intense heat made it impossible for the firemen to stand in the path of the fire and face it with the few streams they had. Wooden buildings caught fire from radiated heat before flame touched them. A storm of burning brands showered every structure ahead of the fire with glowing coals, starting many new fires to leeward. Although there was little wind, the vast rising masses of hot air created convection currents that swept the flames in odd directions. Granite and sandstone and marble were spalled and chipped by the heat, sometimes to the point where they weakened and failed.

The extent of the disaster may be seen from a few statistics. The estimates of monetary loss ranged from $450,000,000 to $1,000,000,000. Over five hundred city blocks were wiped out, covering an area of about three thousand acres. Twenty-eight thousand buildings were destroyed, ranging in size from the shacks of recently arrived immigrants to twenty-story structures downtown.

The number of injuries was tremendous, both from the earthquake and from the fire. Two hundred and sixty-six were killed by the quake, states one report, one hundred and seventy-seven in the fire. Seven were shot by the Regular Army or the militia either while they were looting or by the error of some citizen soldier. Two died of food poisoning as a result of the difficulty in distributing proper rations to the homeless. A hundred thousand refugees thronged into parks and other open places, where quickly organized relief programs of the civil, military, and naval authorities saw to it they were fed and sheltered.

Stops were made that morning at some of the fires that were started by the earthquake, but they availed nothing. The fires that were not stopped grew constantly larger until the spreading flames engulfed those few locations where the firemen had managed to halt the blaze. By this time the closely built wooden residential district was thoroughly involved.

Some of the fire companies fell back to protect the waterfront area, which was the very heart of the economic life of San Francisco. There the failure of the water mains was not a handicap, for the steamers were able to draft salt water from the harbor. They had the assistance of water lines from a fireboat, some Navy tugs, a U.S. Revenue cutter, and several ordinary harbor tugboats. Here where water was available, an excellent stop was made. With many heavy streams they halted the fire before it reached the wharves and warehouses.

On the other side of the fire a stand was made at Market

Street, one hundred and twenty feet wide. Steamers were at the few hydrants still in working order and were pumping from some of the twenty cisterns the city still had. They also pumped from the sewers, which now had some of the water escaping from the many fractured water mains. In this defensive battle, dynamite and gunpowder were freely used to demolish buildings in the path of the flames.

The results were poor. The men with the explosives, generally U.S. Army personnel, blew up buildings next to those already on fire. The effect of this was to create enormous heaps of kindling wood next to structures already fiercely blazing. The fire, in most instances, promptly communicated to the new pile of rubbish. But with the gaps from the few successful explosions, the streams of water from the steamers, the lack of wind, and the width of the street, the Market Street line held.

This success was only temporary. The wind changed and became brisk; flames and burning brands and heat overcame the width of the street and the streams of water. The fight at Market Street was lost, and the conflagration roared into the business district. The fire-fighters retreated in deep discouragement.

Now came a phase of the San Francisco fire that caused tremendous financial loss and yet from which all fire-protection engineers and architects were to learn a very great deal. This phase was the burning of the "fireproof" buildings in the downtown section. The Call Building, an eighteen-story, tower-like structure, caught fire when the flames entered through windows cracked by the intense heat of burning buildings nearby. The flames traveled up elevator shafts and stair wells, and the contents of the building were destroyed.

There was nothing left inside the building, although the walls and frame and floors, built of steel and concrete, remained intact.

So it was with the others of the Class A steel and concrete buildings. They all survived the fire and, after renovation work, continued to be used. These were all structures with a steel skeleton encased in concrete, brick walls, and floors of reinforced concrete. Although the contents burned fiercely and the buildings were subjected to intense heat, they came through the conflagration structurally sound. Nor had the earthquake shocks in any way impaired their integrity. They all, over two dozen of them, were ready after the fire for the plasterers and painters and glaziers to get to work on them.

Here was learned the lesson that a Class A building is not fire safe if it has unprotected window openings. There must be windows with chicken wire between two sheets of glass, metal sash, metal shutters, metal-covered doors and casings, and a tank on the roof to supply water for the sprinklers if the pressure of the public water supply weakens or fails entirely.

A steel beam that is naked fails completely under the heat of a burning building and bends like a wax candle in a hot attic in July and whatever it is supporting collapses. A steel beam must be encased in concrete applied in conformity to rigid specifications if it is to stand up in a fire. Concrete floors and interior walls of tile will fail in a fire if not constructed to Underwriters' specifications. San Francisco demonstrated what had already been proven at Boston; granite does not stand up under intense heat, nor does marble, limestone, or sandstone. These kinds of stone all had to be replaced when San Francisco's burned out Class A buildings were renovated. Terra cotta and pressed brick came through the conflagration much better.

Even though this conflagration seemed unstoppable as it defeated the men making the valiant stand at Market Street, the fighting spirit of the San Franciscans was in no way diminished. Another stand, this one successful, was made at a group composed of the U. S. Mint, the U. S. Post Office, the Montgomery Building, and the Appraiser's stores of the U. S. Customs. In the Mint was $200,000,000 in gold coin, so this fight was for a very big prize indeed.

The Mint had water-storage tanks in the basement, a hand-operated pump, a line of one-inch hose, stout construction, and a group of determined employees. The Montgomery block had thick brick walls and iron shutters on the windows. In the well-constructed post office the loyal employees fought with wet mailbags to keep the fire from entering.

An Oakland engine company was in the battle, and a detail of sailors from the U. S. Revenue cutter *Bear* was an important element in this seven-hour struggle.

The victory was hard-won. Here stood an island in the vast area of destruction: these four important buildings and a few smaller ones. On all sides lay only smoking and flaming ruins. The government employees and volunteers and sailors rested after their long battle and the taste of victory was theirs.

There were several other victorious stops. In each of them the persistence and fighting spirit of the San Franciscans brought success to an extent; a small, very small, part of their beloved city was saved.

The first of these stops was at the house of Mrs. Robert Louis Stevenson, the widow of the great writer. A group of men known as the Bohemian Club, when her house was threatened by the fire, went to assist Mrs. Stevenson. They fought with wet blankets and dirt and what water they could find to keep the fire from entering the building. They succeeded. Persistence, determination, and devoted effort paid off. One may judge from the name of this group that they appreciated a great literary man. They rallied to help the wife of their venerated R.L.S., and their reward was victory when at last the fire in the nearby buildings died down and her house still stood.

Another minor success was gained as the fire swept up Russian Hill, taking numerous mansions of the wealthy. In one great house, whose owner and family were away, an old Civil War veteran who was caretaker fought the never-ceasing storm of burning brands until it appeared to him the fight was lost. He was determined that the house in his care, when it perished, should do so with honor, so he raised the American flag, dipped it three times as a farewell, and prepared to depart.

A nearby company of soldiers who were trying to help fight the conflagration saw the flag, and thinking it flew from a military headquarters, rushed up to the mansion to help defend it. They stayed and fought it out, using a bathtub full of water, wet blankets, and quantity of full soda siphon bottles, and wet earth. With plenty of manpower they won. The mansion was saved and five other houses behind it that were thus spared full exposure to the heat.

Another success was won on Telegraph Hill, not among mansions, but among the shanties of immigrant Italians. To these men, brought up in a country where most men were tenants of big landlords without hope of ever owning anything themselves, a shack of one's own on a California hillside was as a castle. They battled fiercely to save their little wooden houses, crowded in and highly inflammable—about as poor a fire risk as might be imagined.

The Italians used dirt, they used water, and they used great quantities of the red wine of which they are so fond. The wine was stored in barrels in their cellars, and they used it without hesitation, soaking blankets in it and hanging the blankets on their houses to shield them from the heat. Many of the Italian shanties went up in smoke, but many were saved by the desperate defense of these devoted men.

The greatest battlefield of all was Van Ness Avenue, a street one hundred and twenty-five feet wide. Beyond it lay a newer part of the city, the Western Addition, a vast area of residences. If the fire could be halted at Van Ness, the Western Addition was safe, immense property values would be preserved, and a great increase in the number of homeless people would be prevented.

Orders were given to dynamite the entire east side of the street. Enough dynamite did not arrive, so the soldiers set fire to many of the houses, some of them very expensive mansions, and reduced them to ashes before the dread heat wave of the conflagration arrived. Some buildings were blown up, and others were demolished by Army artillery.

Repair crews managed to get one hydrant on Van Ness working, and three steam fire engines were brought to the scene. Another water line was brought to the fire by four engines pumping in relay, the first in the line taking its water from the Bay. When the main front of the conflagration reached Van Ness, it came up against the vast belt where all buildings had been either blown up or burned.

The fire was checked along nearly all the length of Van

Ness. At one point it crossed and fired the steeple of St. Mary's Roman Catholic Church. Men scaled the steeple on the outside, and two priests climbed up inside. They succeeded in chopping away the burning parts of the steeple. The blazing wood dropped to the ground and the church was saved.

At one point the fire crossed Van Ness on a seven-block front in spite of all efforts to check it. Dynamite, which had been very scarce, now arrived in a convoy of U. S. Army wagons. Soldiers, firemen, and volunteers promptly put it to work. In a series of tremendous blasts, seven entire blocks of houses between Van Ness and Franklin Street were flattened. The fire was checked here also.

This was a great victory for the firemen, soldiers, and volunteers who had fought relentlessly on the line of Van Ness. They had saved the Western Addition and the homes of one hundred and fifty thousand people.

There were other stops, although none to equal in magnitude and importance the halting of the fire at Van Ness. Yet the other victories are further demonstration of the fighting spirit and capabilities of the fire department, the Army and Navy units, the countless San Franciscans who volunteered, and the government employees who fought at their posts of duty at great personal risk.

After three and a half days, on Sunday morning, the fire was at last checked everywhere. At no point did it merely burn itself out, as is so often the case with a conflagration. Vast as was the destruction, the fire finally was stopped at numerous points.

A few features should be noted. One is what they termed the "ham and eggs fire." This was one of the many fires early on the first day that got out of hand and united to form the general conflagration. Immediately after the earthquake, a general police order forbade anyone to light a fire in a stove until the safety of the chimney had been determined by an expert examination.

A certain lady either had not heard of the order or decided that no tiresome official rules were to interfere with her morning duty of getting breakfast. She kindled a brisk wood fire in her kitchen stove and proceeded to cook ham and eggs for her lord and master's morning repast. Her chimney had been broken by the quake at a point not visible to her, and the heat and sparks soon started a brisk partition fire. The firemen were all occupied elsewhere, so her house was soon ablaze and the flames were spreading to the houses of neighbors.

The firemen never did get ahead of the ham and eggs fire. It roared through acres of frame buildings before losing its identity by merging with other fires that had got out of hand.

Something of a different nature occurred when great throngs of refugees began to flee the advancing wall of flame, heading for the safety of large public parks. As always happens in time of great stress and emergency, women who were with child discovered that their time had come much sooner than was expected.

There was no arguing with such a situation and many a baby was first heard to cry aloud on a public sidewalk, while the mother was assisted by bystanders who were willing and well intentioned, however much they lacked skill and knowledge. It is recorded that on this day of disaster one man assisted at six deliveries in various spots on the sidewalks of tortured San Francisco.

One might wonder what gave this man the thought that he could be valuable in such a situation. Why he undertook to preside at these events is more understandable when we learn that this old-timer had been a shotgun messenger on a Wells Fargo stagecoach. While his first responsibility in that post had been to fill with lead any robber who tried to take the gold dust from the stage's strongbox, he undoubtedly was accustomed to assisting in other emergencies. This would include doing the needful at childbirth, for any woman at all near her time who traveled over the mountain roads in a Wells Fargo stagecoach would be likely to find nature's processes accelerated by the rough trip. Obviously this old shotgun messenger had been all through this sort of thing before. He was a man of experience, he was needed, he was ready, and in the true spirit of the Old West, he rolled up his sleeves and met the emergency. Six emergencies.

When the fire was at last over, there remained only the task of patrolling the devastated areas, collecting the insurance, and rebuilding the city. Regular Army troops did much of the patrolling to prevent looters from taking over. The state militia also did patrol duty and in their eagerness to preserve order created some rather taut situations. The difficulty was adjusted after some rather acrid interchanges between state, federal, and municipal authorities.

Collecting the insurance was the sad chapter. Faced with losses of $350,000,000, the insurance world was shaken to its very foundations. Some companies stalled and chiseled; some went bankrupt; and two foreign companies defaulted and withdrew from doing business in the United States.

Two local companies did admirably. The California Insurance Company had assets of $450,000 and fire-loss claims of $2,550,000. This looked like bankruptcy and a payment of twenty cents on the dollar to policyholders who had suffered losses. The company levied an assessment on the stockholders and paid in full. The Fireman's Fund Insurance Company had $7,000,000 in assets and $11,500,000 in losses. Here again bankruptcy loomed, but the ingenuity of the Californians was equal to the problem. They liquidated the company, paid fifty-six and a half cents on the dollar, formed a new company, and paid the balance of the claims in stock in the new company.

San Francisco was helped by relief contributions from all over the United States and from foreign countries. This money was used to feed the homeless and destitute. But most of all, San Francisco was helped by the San Franciscans.

The energy, drive, and optimism that had made their city of world importance was in no way damaged by the devastating conflagration which had consumed so much. The building of a new city was soon under way, a city whose structures would bear a much better reputation with the Fire Underwriters.

The rest of the country was amazed by the progress San Francisco made. The Class A steel and concrete buildings, twenty-seven of them, were renovated and reoccupied. New skyscrapers were built. In three years almost all the burned area was rebuilt. Twenty thousand new buildings were erected in this time and the assessed value of the city was 5 percent greater than before the fire. The people of the city considered that this chapter was over. They looked forward to new pages in their history and busied themselves with plans for their World's Fair, which was to celebrate the opening of the Panama Canal.

8

A Cellar Fire in Baltimore

AT TWENTY-THREE MINUTES past ten on February 7, 1904, a quiet Sunday morning, the Baltimore Fire Department headquarters received an automatic alarm from the basement of the Hurst Building, a six-story wholesale dry-goods occupancy in the downtown business district. An engine company and a ladder company were sent to take care of the fire.

The ladder men jimmied the door and found nothing on the first floor except a little smoke. In the basement they discovered a smoky little fire smoldering in a pile of merchandise, so they took a line from a chemical tank, which most of Baltimore's hose wagons carried. When a ladderman began to pull the pile of merchandise apart with a plasterhook, he uncovered a fierce, hot fire that immediately blazed up with a fury that was altogether too much to be handled by a chemical line.

Other piles of dry goods in the basement caught fire at once. It was clear that the whole area would be involved in minutes, so the men with the chemical line, hitting the fire with their small stream as they retreated, backed up to the stairway, shouting for a big water line.

At once the officer in charge ordered a box alarm to be sent in and his men hurried a big line into the building. By the time they got the water, the flames had spread across the piles of dry goods and the entire cellar was burning furiously. The cellar was too hot to enter, so the big water line was aimed down the stairway. From this position it struck only a part of the fire, and the ladder company went to work with axes to open holes in the floor so the engine companies coming in on the box alarm could go to work with cellar pipes.

But before the holes in the floor were opened a terrific "hot air" explosion blew out all the windows of the fifth and sixth floors, and immediately the entire Hurst Building with its six floors loaded with dry goods was ablaze from cellar to roof.

It should be stated here that the expression "hot air" explosion fails to convey an accurate idea of what happens. It is not hot air that explodes; it is a mixture of the gases that come from inflammable materials when they are heated in an enclosed area. Not generally realized is the fact that anything that will burn at all gives off gas when heated. Thus a fire in a cellar full of dry goods where the supply of oxygen is limited mulls along and these materials dissociate. The unburned particles rise in the form of gas and when they reach an area where oxygen is more plentiful, they suddenly ignite, causing an explosion.

When there is the right proportion of oxygen and burnable gasses, it is said to be an "explosive mixture." By creating the right proportion of air and gasoline fumes in a motor and causing ignition by electric sparks, we have a series of small explosions that make an internal combustion engine propel an automobile.

The same principle of chemistry operates when there is a fire in a confined space in a building. The fire burns slowly, i.e., smolders, on what oxygen there is. The heat of the fire converts some of the material into gas, which rises and collects in higher parts of the building. It must be remembered that there are as many varieties of gas as there are combustible materials. Wood gas is the most common, always present when wood is heated. In a fireplace, oxygen being available, the gas burns brightly around the logs. Actually it is the wood gas which is burning, not the logs. They are hot, and are being cooked until their elements are vaporized (or gasified). It is the gas that burns.

The foregoing serves to explain what occurred in the Hurst Building in Baltimore that quiet winter Sunday morning in 1904. The gas rose in the elevator shaft, oxygen mixed with it in the right proportion, the flames of the cellar fire ignited it, and the whole collection of gas, permeating the shaft and the top stories, burned quickly and all at once.

The explosion was of terrific force. It blew out not only all the windows in the fifth and sixth floors but most of the windows in several nearby buildings. Following the explosion there was a vast surge of fire, turning the upper part of the Hurst Building into a flaming torch. The nearby structures, their windows blown out, were soon afire, and a twenty-mile-an-hour breeze carried the flames to the stacks of inflammable merchandise stored within. In an instant a brisk cellar fire, which a one-alarm assignment of fire apparatus could easily handle, had become a major fire of the utmost seriousness. Then a safe on a nearby sidewalk, containing sixty pounds of gunpowder, exploded, breaking even more windows. The safe was kept on the sidewalk in front of a hardware store because it was thought too dangerous to have gunpowder inside the store. As it turned out, it could not have been put in a worse place.

The chief realized at once that this one was entirely out of hand. He ordered the second, the third, and the fourth alarms as quickly as the fire-alarm telegraph could handle them. Then he ordered the general alarm, which called every piece of apparatus in Baltimore to the scene, even to the most remote chemical engine in a faraway suburb. This gave him twenty-nine steamers with their hose wagons and eight ladder trucks. Still the fire continued to spread.

At this time overhead electric wires, burned off buildings and poles, began to fall, creating additional obstacles for the firemen in their desperate battle. A charged wire struck the chief. Completely disabled, he was rushed to a hospital. For him the battle was over.

To his successor in command fell the decisions as to fighting what was now plainly a conflagration wholly out of control and beyond the capabilities of the Baltimore Fire Department, which was a big one and a good one. He gave orders to send for out-of-town help.

In 1904 there was no way of responding to a call for help from a distant city except by railroad. However, this was done with efficiency and dispatch. A message to the railroad and everyone in the organization turned to the task of preparing an emergency run. Flatcars were spotted on a track in the freight yard. Inclined planks or runways were set up so the heavy steamers and their hose wagons could be manhandled aboard. A cattle car was provided for the horses, a coach for the firemen.

One of the railroad's best locomotives backed down from the roundhouse and coupled on to the head end by the time the fire engines were loaded aboard. Before the train pulled out of the freight yard the dispatcher would see to it that the tracks were clear all the way to the city where the disaster of fire had taken charge. The telegraph wires hummed with orders for every other train to get into the nearest sidetrack.

Slow freights, local passenger trains, the fast *Limited* that usually had rights over other trains—all were off the main line and in sidings. After the special with the fire engines had rocketed by, throttle wide open, whistle warning all ahead that it was coming, the normal operation of the railroad resumed. The freights, the locals, and the *Limited* crawled out of their sidetracks and business went on as usual.

As a result of Baltimore's messages of distress more than thirty out-of-town steam fire engines and their hose wagons came to help. Except for those from nearby towns, all traveled on special railroad trains. Washington, Philadelphia, Wilmington, Harrisburg, and Atlantic City sent one or more steamers. Apparatus came from Annapolis, Sparrows Point, Relay, and St. Denis, all in Maryland, and from Chester, York, Altoona, and Phoenixville in Pennsylvania.

The most spectacular run of all was from New York City. Nine steamers and hose wagons were rolled aboard a special train in the yards in Jersey City and away they went to Baltimore, with rights over everything else on the road.

While out-of-town help speeded toward Baltimore, the fire situation steadily worsened. The area surrounding the Hurst Building contained old brick buildings with wooden interiors and no window protection. Some had formerly been residences. The streets were narrow. After several buildings had become involved, the heat was so intense that structures downwind caught fire before the flames touched them. The wind was blowing at twenty miles an hour, gusting to thirty, pushing the body of heat toward the buildings to leeward and carrying vast quantities of burning brands and embers to drop onto all manner of inflammable material as much as a half mile from the fire.

The rapidity with which the fire spread, the intense heat, the swiftness with which buildings became involved, stunned the fire-fighters. Ordinary hose streams, even with all the pressure a hard-working steamer could furnish, did not reach the fire. They turned to steam before they hit the burning structures. Baltimore's Engine 15 and Ladder 2, the two pieces of apparatus that responded to the automatic alarm, were so near the Hurst Building that they were wrecked by the explosion. There they stayed, partially buried by the rubble from falling walls, and their part in the terrific drama was over.

The fire now had the usual conflagration pattern. It was impossible for the firemen to make a stand in front of it. Streams did not reach. Buildings in the path of the fire were suddenly alight all over, often before the flames reached them. Modern steel and concrete buildings without shutters or wired glass to protect the windows were no obstacle to the fire. The flames entered on the windward side, the contents burned furiously, the fire roared out of the leeward side and into the next building.

Downwind there was a storm of burning brands, some six inches long. This always occurs in a conflagration. The burning fragments in such a fire storm do much to spread the conflagration. They descend in volume on wooden surfaces, such as shingle roofs, gutters, stairs, piazza floors. They collect until there are enough of them to cook a steak, and the heat from such a mass of coals is enough to set fire to most wooden structures.

People in the path of these embers found their coats and hats were glowing in spots where a fiery fragment had rested. In that era many men wore celluloid collars, a clothing item both inexpensive and easy to clean. In Baltimore that day several serious cases of burns resulted because hot embers had ignited celluloid collars worn by men who were watching the fire from what they thought was a safe distance.

As has happened in most conflagrations, dynamiting buildings was urged by some city officials. The desperate situation of the city led others to agree to a trial of dynamiting buildings in the path of the fire. And as has happened in most conflagrations, the dynamite explosions did nothing to halt the fire. Many windows were broken ahead of the fire by the blasts, sparks and brands entered where the windows were broken, and the building was soon on fire.

In the year 1904 hose couplings were not standard as they are today. The cities had varying couplings, which meant that many of the steamers coming from other cities could not connect to Baltimore hydrants. This was a very considerable setback, since as a result many of the fire engines that had come long distances were useless.

They stood at the sides of the streets, doing nothing while the fire marched inexorably onward through downtown Baltimore. The problem was solved by some out-of-town companies who found horse troughs or half barrels, placed them under the big gate on the hydrants, turned on the water, and thus made reservoirs from which the steamers could draft and get water to work with.

The real solution of the situation of diverse couplings came when it was decided to make a stand at a small river called Jones Falls. This canal-like stream, fifty feet wide, went through part of the city and was bridged in several places. Here the water made an excellent fire break. Here, for the first time, was an opportunity for the more than thirty out-of-town fire engines to work without any dependence on hydrants, for they could take suction from the river.

Some of the Baltimore steamers and most of the out-of-town steamers assembled on the other side of Jones Falls, the out-of-town engines dropping their big suction hoses into the river. Forty steam fire engines were assembled here, each capable of pumping at least two streams.

At last there was together, in front of the fire, enough apparatus to deliver a real blow, for eighty streams of water is a tremendous force. The conflagration roared down to the bank of Jones Falls. The forty steamers were all at work, pumping at full speed, rocking up and down on their springs and punching straight columns of black smoke straight upward. Men who can remember the action and vitality of a steam fire engine working at full speed, the measured beat of the cylinders, the roar of the exhaust in the smokestacks, the flashing piston rods and the brass fly wheel turning so fast it is a blur may form, in the mind's eye, a picture of this concentration of forty steamers along this little stream. And any real fireman who gets deep satisfaction in seeing a strong, straight stream lancing into a tough fire can imagine this epic scene, where at last it was possible to meet the fire head on.

At selected points the firemen, helmets reversed so the broad tails shielded their faces from the heat, manned eighty powerful engine lines. Here they fought it out with their mighty antagonist. And here they won, for at Jones Falls the nine steamers from New York and all the other steamers were able to put up a volume of water that halted the Baltimore fire in its tracks.

Many a fireman or spark or buff, reading of this epic fight, has envied those who were there when the conflagration was beaten at Jones Falls. To fight fire is, they feel, a fine experience, but to win is glorious. The records tell us that this fire was fought by seventeen hundred firemen, including four hundred "unattached volunteers."

The storm of red embers set a number of fires in the area beyond Jones Falls. This had been foreseen. There were chemical companies and detached engine companies that dealt with these fires before they could develop.

So at last they had it out, or at least confined where it could spread no more. Ruins within the lines glowed and blazed until the firemen got around to soaking them, but the dangerous part was over. The buildings of eighty city blocks had vanished in the roaring flames, and the battle had gone on for thirty hours, so it was Monday afternoon before the firemen could say they had stopped it.

One hundred and fifty-five acres were devastated, twenty-five hundred buildings were destroyed, fifty thousand people were out of work, and the property loss was $50,000,000.

In the Baltimore fire we find lacking some of the factors which have combined to give a start to other conflagrations we have considered. There was no delayed alarm. Word of this fire came by automatic alarm, which is the fastest. There was no extra hazardous situation, such as the aggregation of shanties dried out by weeks of drought at Chicago.

There was no injury to the water supply or any event which started simultaneous fires, as at San Francisco. There were no conditions impairing the efficiency of the fire department as at Boston and Chicago. Some unfavorable conditions there were. The hot-air explosion soon after the arrival of the fire department changed this from a minor fire that could be handled by a one-alarm assignment into a big fire involving six buildings and requiring the entire fire department.

A brisk wind helped to carry this fire into other buildings, as it always does. The type of construction in this area was very poor; old-fashioned, inflammable, and with no installations to retard the spread of fire.

Besides the final stop made by the massive assemblage of forty steamers at Jones Falls, a brilliant stop made at a warehouse on one side of the fire should be mentioned. Here, as in similar instances at Boston and at San Francisco, loyal employees gathered to help in the battle. Men were on the roof to wet down embers as they fell and hang wet blankets over the cornices. Other men inside hung wet blankets over windows.

They started the house pump and overflowed a tank on the roof. Then they plugged up the holes in the gutters so the water flowing off the roof would not go into the downspouts or roof drains. The result was that the water overflowed the gutters and formed a curtain down the outside of the building. The cooling effect of the water curtain protected the windows from breakage and prevented the wooden window sash, sills, and frames from catching fire. This alert crew saved the building in which they worked and as their reward they had jobs the day after the fire, whereas thousands of others were out of work.

Civilized nations would scarcely merit the term did they not learn from such a gigantic disaster as the Baltimore fire. The lessons learned here were several.

Lesson Number One. It is imperative that there be standard hose couplings, so the fire apparatus from one community may work in another in the time of a disastrous fire. In Baltimore the difference in couplings destroyed much of the value of the out-of-town fire apparatus sent by so many other cities at great effort. The transportation of these fire engines over the railroads was a superb example of coordination and cooperation, yet when they arrived, many of them had to stand idle because they could not connect to Baltimore hydrants. Finally they were able to be of use when it was decided to make a stand at Jones Falls, and there they drafted from the river, laid their own hose lines, and thus were independent of the Baltimore hydrants. Under the leadership of the National Fire Protection Association, hose and hydrant couplings were made standard shortly thereafter. So this lesson was learned.

Lesson Number Two. Electric wires should be underground. A power line, burned from a building, fell on the chief of the Baltimore Fire Department, disabling him. Falling wires were a constant danger to the men throughout this fire. This lesson has been largely learned. In most large cities, the wires in downtown areas are underground.

Lesson Number Three. Whenever possible, streets should be widened and open spaces such as squares and small parks created. We have seen that in every conflagration, one of the great factors in the spread of the fire has been the volume of intense heat, sometimes enough to cause a building to burst into flames before the actual fire reaches it. The more open area there is, the more the heat is reduced and dissipated before it reaches the next building.

Lesson Number Four. Vertical openings in buildings, such as stairways, elevator wells, and rubbish and laundry chutes should be protected by self-closing trap doors or by sprinkler heads or by both. It was by way of unprotected vertical openings that the unburned gasses from the fire in the cellar of the Hurst Building rose to charge the upper stories and finally explode when the right mixture of gas and air occurred.

Lesson Number Five. Every fire department should be well provided with large-stream appliances. The favorite is a deluge set which takes in three lines and delivers one massive stream. This is sometimes called a gun.

Even better is a hose wagon mounting a deluge set or wagon gun or deck gun which takes in three or more streams and delivers one big stream of tremendous reach and power. This is a fixed appliance on the hose wagon and can therefore be operated by one man. If it should be necessary to retreat, the gun may be left in position, still delivering an enormous quantity of water to break the heat of the fire and hold it in check.

Every fire department should contemplate the possibility that it may someday be faced with a conflagration or be asked to assist at one. Few firemen have ever seen a conflagration, yet it is well established that only streams of great reach and power are of value in such an emergency. Therefore, one or more deck guns should be part of every department's equipment.

A deck gun should be mounted on an *independent* vehicle and *not* on the pumping engine. A pump's place is at the hydrant and that is where they always go upon arrival at the fire. Then, if a deck gun is needed and the pump is working at a hydrant, much confusion results in shutting down the pump, ordering the men manning its lines to back out and then moving the pump to a position from which its gun can hit the fire. This maneuver results in the loss of the pumping power of that particular pump.

Another way of getting a stream that will reach a fire that is too hot to stand up to is to use the pipe on the tip of an aerial ladder. Usually an aerial ladder has a siamese to take two lines at the bottom, a hose line running up the ladder, and a brass nozzle at the top from which the stream issues.

The primary use of a ladder pipe is to put a stream into the window on the seventh or eighth or ninth story. Then it is used as a water tower. If the playpipe on the ladder tip can be pointed by using control wires at the base of the ladder, it is possible to gain much more reach with a stream by extending the ladder at an angle and thus directing the stream into an area hotter than men with a hand line could bear to face. This use of an aerial ladder could be important in a conflagration.

That is the story of Baltimore's conflagration. It should be added that it was the city's good fortune that no lives were lost. The leadership in Baltimore was excellent; the burned area was soon being rebuilt, the streets widened under the direction of a civic body known as the Burnt District Commission. A fine city was built in this area where much that was old and obsolete was swept away on that winter day in 1904.

9

Palm Sunday in Chelsea

ON PALM SUNDAY, April 12, 1908, in Chelsea, Massachusetts, an alarm was sounded at church time for a dump fire in the so-called "rag district," an area where the junk business was concentrated. The establishments there occupied wooden buildings of the poorest type, "quick burners" as firemen term them.

A high wind, thirty miles an hour, was blowing this April morning. Sparks and burning fragments from the dump fire were carried considerable distances, and by the time the first apparatus arrived, the windward side of a nearby blacking factory was involved. This the fire department managed to get under control, but they then got word that a three-story frame building two blocks down wind used for rag and waste-paper storage had a fire in the yard.

The chief dispatched a chemical company, which got the

better of the fire in the bales of rags and waste paper in the yard. The crew of the chemical company were then astounded to see that another fire had somehow started inside the three-story building and the office space was thoroughly involved. The officer at once sent a man to notify the chief, who was now directing his men to pick up at the first fire.

The chemical company, pending the arrival of the steamers, did their best with what they had. However, a brisk fire in a three-story junk shop on a windy day is too much for any chemical engine and this outfit had already used part of their charge on the fire in the yard. By the time the steamers arrived, the fire, the origin of which was never satisfactorily accounted for, had involved the entire building.

Flames were roaring through the roof and from the windows. Sparks and good-sized burning brands rose in a fiery cloud and were whipped to leeward by the half gale, descending on shingle roofs, on porches, and into the papers and rags stored in the numerous junk establishments in the area. A wooden shed in which gasoline was stored caught fire, burned furiously, and then exploded, flinging burning fragments in all directions.

The chief sent in the second alarm at once, bringing the rest of the Chelsea department. By the time they arrived it was clear to the chief that the fire was entirely out of hand. The conflagration pattern was obvious. Buildings were catching fire every minute, and the burning area was rapidly increasing. The heat to leeward was such that his men could not face it with an ordinary engine line. A dreadful cloud of red-hot sparks and burning embers swirled down wind to ignite buildings several blocks ahead of the main fire.

And when a roof or a porch or a lumber pile caught fire

from burning brands, there was not a piece of apparatus in the Chelsea Fire Department to spare to deal with it. They were all desperately busy; fully engaged in fighting at one or another spot in this far-flung inferno. So when another roof began to burn, the fire developed unchecked. It soon involved nearby buildings, and then another uncontrolled fire was under way and before long had spread enough to join the general conflagration that was marching through the city.

Junk storage buildings, lumber yards, houses, churches, schools, factories, and business buildings melted away as the great fire progressed across the city. The chief had early realized what he was up against and within a half hour of the first alarm, he began to call for out-of-town help. Fire apparatus from two dozen of the municipalities of eastern Massachusetts arrived in Chelsea to help.

With all these extra engine companies, the chief decided to make a stand at Arlington Street. With the streams from a score of hard-working steamers they met the fire in a head-on battle. They lost. The fire rolled on.

By this time it had developed such volume and such heat that no such head-on attack could prevail. The heat warped and bent the street car rails set in the pavements. It melted glass and metal and made granite in curbstones and building stones explode and crumble.

Most of the engine companies took positions at the sides of the fire, not attempting to face the flames frontally, but using their streams to keep the conflagration from spreading laterally. In this they largely succeeded. On a front three quarters of a mile wide the conflagration devoured everything in its path, heading for Chelsea Creek, a small tidal inlet beyond which lay East Boston, another community of wooden three-decker tenement houses, small dwellings, factories, and wharves.

Boston had a sizable contingent of apparatus in Chelsea itself, fighting the main fire. Now the Boston chief realized he had a second problem; the defense of part of his own city. Already a vast cloud of burning embers was descending on East Boston. There, too, were hundreds of wooden shingle roofs, wooden porches and gutters and stairways, and inflammable materials in back yards.

In East Boston, engine companies and chemical companies raced from one spark-set fire to another. They were now taking the brunt of this fire storm, but other towns were feeling it. Fires started in Winthrop and in Nantasket, miles away, set by wind borne embers.

The two hundred fires the embers set in East Boston were handled well by the Boston Fire Department. However, their problems did not end there. On the Chelsea side of the creek were several oil-storage plants. The conflagration roared down on them unchecked. Oil tanks soon were flaming torches. Their steel sides ruptured, and the flaming oil poured into Chelsea Creek. Soon the surface of the water was a sheet of flame as the floating oil from the tanks burned.

In this hellish maelstrom was a Boston fireboat that had been hitting the oncoming conflagration with several powerful streams from the big monitor nozzles mounted on its deck. Now the flames from the burning oil on the water surrounded the fireboat. It seemed doomed. Fiery death beckoned to its crewmen. With the fireboat fighting for its life, the captain ordered the streams from its monitor nozzles turned upon the surface of the waters dead ahead. The torrents of water, driven by every ounce of power in the boat's big pumps, swept back the flames and opened a clear path.

The captain rang for full speed ahead. The fireboat forged forward, its stream still playing into the waters in front of the bow. As she steamed through the flames, heat blistered the paint on her sides and cracked the glass in the pilot-house windows.

At last she was free of this mortal danger, beyond the oil flaming on the face of the waters. Beyond, yet not far beyond, the fireboat halted and again turned her heavy streams on the burning structures on the Chelsea shore.

But this day's troubles for the Boston Fire Department were not over. An oil barge on the Chelsea shore, burning furiously, parted her hawsers and drifted across the creek toward the Standard Oil storage plant on the East Boston Side. She struck. The flames from her burning cargo leaped to the buildings and tanks of the Standard Oil plant and soon a raging fire roared through the place.

More Boston engines came over from the city itself to join the desperate fight to contain the fire and prevent it from sweeping through East Boston's crowded wooden buildings. Here was a battle won. Although the heat from the burning oil plant was bad enough, it did not have added to it the heat of the conflagration, for the width of the creek, full of cold ocean water, was enough to dissipate much of the heat. The streams from the fireboat had done much to reduce the heat, the width of the creek did more, and the powerful streams of the Boston Department did the rest. In a face to face fight, the firemen won out, the conflagration was halted; East Boston was saved.

That is the end of the account of the progress of the conflagration through the closely built city of Chelsea, an area so near Boston that it is called part of Greater Boston. There is more to the story; various happenings that serve to show those who have never witnessed a conflagration what such an experience is like.

This day there were 17,000 homeless, most of whom had been able to save nothing. Many moved household belongings into a park, only to see their property consumed when the fire reached the park. They fled before the great wave of heat, counting themselves fortunate to be alive.

Some tried to save a mattress and many a man struggled down the street with this load on his back only to discover that the hail of burning embers had set fire to his burden. Then he had to throw it down, let the mattress burn, and go sorrowfully on his way—now with nothing whatsoever.

The militia were called to keep order, patrol the ruins, and prevent looting and thievery. To them fell the duty of caring for these homeless and hungry thousands. Seven hundred army tents were pitched to shelter the refugees, and field kitchens were set up in town to feed them.

One Chelsea resident had better luck in saving his household goods. Eli C. Bliss, one of the more substantial citizens, had some very fine furniture, including antiques. With horrified gaze he watched the approaching disaster. The glowing embers rained down upon his house, and the roof smoldered. No piece of fire apparatus was near to help him. Bliss knew that in another half hour his house and furniture would be ashes.

The house was situated beside the tracks of the Boston & Maine Railroad, and as Bliss stared at the advancing wall of flame he noticed a local freight train approaching at a slow rate of speed. The train crew were watching the fire that was approaching the tracks.

A thought flashed into his mind. Bliss ran down the slope to the tracks and waved his arms. The train stopped. He shouted his message to the train crew; he told them he was about to lose everything.

The five railroad men jumped to the ground, ran up the slope, and dashed into the house to get the furniture. Bliss and the five men managed to drag most of the furniture out of the house, down the slope and put it into an empty freight car. The conductor noticed that the wooden sides of some of the cars were beginning to smoke from the heat of the conflagration, which had now reached the other edge of the railroad right of way.

He gave the engineer the highball and as he swung onto the step of the caboose, he took a final look at the residence of Eli C. Bliss. The entire roof was ablaze.

Mr. Bliss received word a few days later that his furniture was in the railroad freight house at Newburyport, where the train crew had unloaded it at the end of their run. He was probably the only man in Chelsea who was burned out and yet managed to save any considerable part of his personal effects.

As always in a conflagration, the out-of-town firemen were a major factor in the fight. Chelsea's three steamers were reinforced by twenty-seven others, so that thirty were trying to halt this vast fire, besides another six of Boston's steamers, some chemical companies, and the fireboat engaged in the struggle to save East Boston. The Boston department lost two steamers in Chelsea, overwhelmed by the fire.

The experiences of two of these out-of-town steamers give

an idea of what it was like in Chelsea that Palm Sunday in the year 1908. The call for help reached Lynn early, soon after the Chelsea chief realized he was dealing with a conflagration. Engine 3, a light two-horse Amoskeag steamer, and its hose wagon made the five-mile run across the wide marsh and through Revere to the fire scene.

Following was Engine 1, a three-horse Metropolitan steamer and its hose wagon. On a response such as this, the engines did not come galloping onto the scene as was usual on a short run in their own city. Trotting part of the time and walking part of the time was the pace on a five-mile journey if the driver wanted to get there at all. Horses driven such a distance at speed have been known to drop dead in harness.

Lynn's Engine 3 took a hydrant on Broadway on the north side of the fire, toward Revere, using their two lines to keep the fire from working sideways and widening its path. Here they were joined by Medford's Engine 4 and the two companies slugged it out with the fire in a livery stable and a couple of store buildings.

They won; the fire progressed no farther in this direction in this area. The stable and the store buildings were wrecks, but the point to be noted is that here they made a stop. In the science of fire-fighting the all important objective is that the fire be halted, and if the building in which it is stopped is a charred and tangled ruin, yet it is nevertheless a victory because the fire is stopped.

We might remark here upon the considerable number of people who upon viewing the ruins of a building after the fire department has returned to quarters come forth with the opinion that it would have been better to have allowed it to burn clean so as to save the big job of rubbish removal. The folly of this notion is well illustrated by the desperate fight Lynn's Engine 3 and the Medford steamer put up at Broadway.

The Chelsea conflagration was traveling fast. It was spreading by burning brands carried by a strong wind and it was spreading by radiated heat. Had the firemen tried to manage the burning stable and stores so as to provide someone later on with a cleaned up building site, they might have discovered that the radiated heat had set fire to the next building. Or a slight shift in the wind could have sent the storm of burning brands into an area as yet untouched.

Then the conflagration would have extended, more of the city would have been overwhelmed by fire, and on this front there would have been defeat instead of victory. These firemen were intent on but one thing; to get the fire out no matter what ruin existed when they were through.

Also, note carefully that these crews fought at the side of the fire. Had they tried to face it head on, the intensity of the heat would have been too much for them, and they would have been obliged to retreat. Over on Bellingham Hill Engine 1's men faced the fire. They lost their steamer and their hose and retreated, having accomplished nothing.

There are a few of what might be called footnotes to the story of the swath of fire through Chelsea and the destruction of factories, stores, churches, schools, and the buildings that had been homes for seventeen thousand people. The Boston & Maine Railroad did valiant work for others than Mr. Bliss, whose good fortune we have mentioned, when they ran flatcars into the fire area to receive the belongings of any one who put them aboard. A considerable quantity of household furniture was saved by these railroad cars, which, as soon as they had a load, were pulled out of the fire zone by a locomotive and placed in a position of safety. The locomotive would then return to the fire area with more empty cars.

A few fortunate people managed to save something substantial by taking advantage of the railroad flatcars. The majority of the Chelsea inhabitants fled with what they could pick up as they hurried out of the house. One man had only his laundry bundle. A ten-year-old boy escaped with a brown hen under each arm and his sister had a gray-and-white cat.

Looters there were, hoping to steal property that owners had carried to a park or some other safe place. The militia and the police arrested some of them—the lucky ones. The looters caught in thievery by the citizens who had been burned out had a hard time of it, and when rescued by police or soldiers were often in a semiconscious condition.

Chelsea was a city where the collecting of rags and junk was practically a major industry. In fact, the involvement of the so-called rag district gave the fire the impetus that made it become a conflagration. Hundreds of junk men lived in Chelsea. Each one had his horse and wagon with which each day he drove through some part of the two dozen cities and towns of Metropolitan Boston, up one street, down the next. His odd and distinctive call told the householders that the junkie was on the street ready to buy scrap iron, paper or rags.

At day's end the junkie would drive back to Chelsea, his wagon loaded, to dispose of his collection to one of the big operators. The junkies, mostly immigrants from Eastern Europe, fared better than most in saving their possessions. It was

Sunday and they were home. Sensing the immensity of the disaster, they harnessed their horses to their wagons and loaded on their furniture and other belongings.

Traveling northeast through Revere and out onto the long road across the miles of the Lynn marshes were dozens of these one-horse wagons piled high with furniture, the numerous children perched upon the load and the good wife on the front seat, holding the baby. Behind them the night sky glowed with the angry red of a burning city.

This seemed less strange to them than to the native born Americans. They had heard the old folks in Europe tell of flight when wars or massive persecutions rent the land. Many of these junkmen had been born in Russia. In that country a grandfather's tale had often told of flight, burning cities, and pursuit and persecution.

Here was flight, but no pursuit or persecution. Refugees were protected people. The old horse plodded along the road across the great marsh, and they were safe. In the towns on the other side of the marsh were, here and there, friends and relatives from the old country, shelter, food, opportunity to start in anew. And here on the wagon, unharmed, were the furniture and household goods for which they had worked so hard. Every one was together; all of the loved ones. These men from the old countries of Europe knew it could have been much worse.

In the dawn of that April morning there was a lot of traffic moving on the marsh road, all headed toward Lynn. The junk wagons with their loads and their people appeared here and there on the long highway. Engine 3 of Lynn and its hose wagon loaded with wet hose and soot-streaked firemen were headed back to quarters. Lynn Engine 1's hose wagon, empty of hose, carried a company of gloomy firemen and tethered to the hose wagon's rear were the steamer's three horses.

All were on the move except the trolley cars. When the Chelsea fire destroyed the wires, the power went off. Five streetcars on the marsh, and others in Revere, stopped and remained where they were all night, motionless and empty. There they would remain until repair crews managed to get power in the wires once again.

10

Path of Fire across Salem

THE CONFLAGRATION which made a path of fire across Salem, Massachusetts, on June 25, 1914, began near the famous old seaport's boundary with Peabody. Here at Blubber Hollow on the northwest side of town is one of the points farthest from the sea. The fire marched all the way across the city until it reached salt water at the harbor. Only the Atlantic Ocean stopped this conflagration that had traveled the entire breadth of Salem.

As is always the case with a fire that gets completely away, there was at Salem a combination of adverse factors. The day was windy. It had not rained for many days, so wood shingle roofs, wooden stairs and porches, and other parts of buildings where glowing embers might lodge were bone dry. One of the hydrants would not function properly and the second engine to arrive lost time moving to another hydrant. The city had a routine of letting the firemen, alternately, go home to dinner. Of twenty-three permanent men, five were off duty and nine were at dinner. Only nine men were on duty in the entire department when the alarm hit at 1:37 P.M. This, of course, left them dependent on the call men, whose duty it is to hurry to the scene when they hear the alarm or who are picked up by the apparatus on the way to the fire.

The Korn Leather Company on Boston Street, down in a section known as Blubber Hollow, occupied a wooden factory building without sprinklers. In one of their processes for manufacturing leather, they used a mixture of acetone, amylacetate, and alcohol, a touchy group of chemicals. For other work they had on hand a considerable quantity of celluloid. The very recital of the foregoing is enough to make one who knows anything at all about the fire game nervous.

The inevitable happened. Somehow, about half-past one this day, a fire started in this devilish array of hazards. There was an explosion almost immediately. Flames shot up the elevator shaft to the third floor and spread there. The workers ran for their lives.

When the fire department arrived, the Korn Leather Company was completely involved. Flames poured out of the building with that rolling, churning motion so familiar to all who have seen a really tough one that is thoroughly out of hand. The first engine to go to work had to retreat because of the heat and was hauled away by hand. By the time the firemen got their lines laid and some streams on this inferno, the fire had spread to the factory on the east and the factory on the west and had jumped Boston Street to catch a building there. When a fire crosses a street, it means that intense heat has developed.

The first alarm was received at 1:37 P.M. The second or general alarm was sounded at 1:41 P.M., four minutes later, which means that the chief called out all the apparatus in the city as soon as he had one look at this fire. And it was not long after this that the chief began sending calls to other towns for help, a procedure that he continued until fire engines from twenty-one communities had arrived and were working shoulder to shoulder with the Salem Fire Department.

No one could say that the Salem chief was slow about calling for help. The signal went out to Peabody, the nearest town, four minutes after the Salem general alarm. Five minutes later the call went to Beverly. Another three minutes and Lynn was asked to help, and shortly after Swampscott and Marblehead. All these communities border on Salem, and they were all called within a half hour of the first alarm.

Within another half hour Boston, fifteen miles away, had responded with steamers and hose wagons sent by rail. Later Boston sent more and finally had five engine companies at work in Salem.

Before the out-of-town engines got to work, the fire was acting as all conflagrations do. Quickly it spread to one building after another, and the firemen at no time were able to get ahead of it. So many were the buildings demanding attention, that the firemen could not cover them all and some burned without a line being turned on them.

From these fiercely burning structures rose clouds of burning brands and embers by the millions to swirl down wind in a veritable fire storm. They descended on wooden shingle roofs. They drifted against wooden steps and into lattice

From Hingham, a dozen miles south of Boston, came two automobiles crowded with firemen. No call for help was sent Hingham, but word of the disaster had reached town. These men knew a serious fire was in progress and that was all they needed to know. They piled into the automobiles of two of their number, heading for Salem, nor were they far on their way before they saw the great cloud of smoke in the sky. They knew they would be needed.

In Salem the Hingham men quickly found a point on the edge of the fire where they could be useful. Using rugs and blankets and forming a bucket brigade they worked on a house threatened by radiated heat and burning brands. No hose line was available, yet these volunteers managed to save the house and prevent the fire from widening at this location. When the danger there was over, they moved on with their rugs and blankets and buckets to defend another threatened dwelling.

This group is typical of the work of hundreds of determined men and women at Salem. One admires the terrific impact of apparatus such as Hose 5 of Lawrence, but everyone should remember that each pail or kettle of water, each wet rug has value. There was much more of Salem that could have burned, including the business district and whole streets of fine old houses that are choice historical structures. That this part of the city did not burn is due to the hard-fighting firemen from two dozen communities and the hundreds of volunteers who never quit while there was opportunity to carry one more bucket of water or throw one more shovelful of earth.

One of the most effective groups of volunteers was the city laborers who activated the two-horse spraying machine used to apply arsenate of lead to shade trees to kill gypsy moths. A five-hundred-gallon tank and a gasoline piston pump capable of putting a stream into the top of a tall elm tree made this very effective in fighting roof fires. When the tank was empty the men refilled it at the nearest hydrant and continued.

Less fortunate was the experience of the Salem "combination," a piece of motor apparatus with enough big hose to lay one hydrant line and two thirty-five-gallon chemical tanks. A chemical line is an excellent means of dealing with a roof fire. The pressure carries the stream to the roof of the ordinary two-and-a-half-story house and the liquid sticks well to the surface.

The Salem combination's crew used their equipment wisely. They carefully turned off their stream as soon as one patch of burning shingles was extinguished and moved to the next one, opened the nozzle, and with plenty of gas pressure still in the tank, they were able to get an effective stream. With two tanks they were able to deal with a number of roof fires.

When both tanks were empty, they used their spare charge, a bottle of sulphuric acid and a container of sodium bicarbonate, both carried on the kit. Filling the tanks at a hydrant, they went on with their work.

However, when the second charge was used up, they had to return to their fire station for more sulphuric acid and "sody." One of the men, days later, said that when they finally had their reload and returned to the fire scene, the houses where they had extinguished roof fires now had new roof fires of such extent that only an engine line could have handled them, and there were no engine lines available at that point.

This experience illustrates the chief weakness of the chemical tank in fire fighting. Its stream is excellent for small fires, but when it is empty it is a time-consuming operation to recharge it. In that day, engineering had not developed a small pump capable of pumping from a water tank carried on the apparatus.

Today we have the booster pump. The tank of water is much larger than most chemical tanks, and the pump delivers an excellent stream through ordinary chemical hose, which is a little larger than garden hose. When the tank is empty it can be refilled speedily at a nearby hydrant so the fire engine can carry on the fight without leaving the fire scene.

For a fire department that has to cover rural areas, the water tank has the further advantage that volunteers at the fire can bring water in any available receptacle and pour it into the tank through the trap in the top while the pump is working. Some rural apparatus today has water tanks of a five hundred gallon or more capacity. In a tough fight in the country the extra water brought by the volunteers from a well, a brook, or a pond is the difference between victory and defeat.

It is to be remembered that at a fire in the country, everyone is expected to do something. Spectators who merely stand and stare may be spoken to roughly. This also applies to grass and forest fires. Let no one approach the fire scene unless he is ready to go to work.

One of the best stops in the Salem fire was at the LeFavor shoe factory on Canal Street. Plenty of good, hard fire-fighting figured in this success, yet it is instructive to note that here the firemen were assisted by some excellent construction features. This factory had a good fire wall and sprinklers; more help than the firemen had anywhere else in town on this wild and furious afternoon and evening. They saved two thirds of this three-story mill building and work was resumed a few days later.

The final act in the grim and fiery drama at Salem took place at the water's edge in the several buildings of the Naumkeag Steam Cotton Company, situated on Salem Harbor. These mill buildings were well sprinklered both in the interior and on the outside with "open" sprinklers to give a water curtain to protect against exposure to a fire originating outside the building. Water was obtained from a good city main and two one-thousand-gallon-a-minute stationary pumps that took suction from the South River, which here is part of the harbor.

The Naumkeag mills were on a point of land. On three sides was the harbor, on the landward side a closely built residential area of three deckers, a place where the buildings were so close that it would be difficult to find room to swing a cat by the tail. The Naumkeag had a well-organized plant fire department; men who ordinarily worked at various processes in the factories but who reported for fire duty when the whistle blew.

The whistle blew this day when it was seen that this conflagration was inexorably marching across the city. The mill fire brigade were all on duty and around five o'clock they were joined by Edward V. French from the Arkwright Mutual Fire Insurance Company, which carried the policies on the Naumkeag, and Mr. Teague of the Factory Mutual Inspection Department.

These two men were well-known experts in the field of fire protection and they led the defense. At this time the wind direction was such that the Naumkeag buildings did not seem threatened. The workers had been sent home, hose lines were laid out, the big stationary pumps were started. Mill firemen were on the roofs to take care of burning brands, but there was no problem because the wind was not directly toward the Naumkeag.

Another problem now appeared. Some of the men could see the fire approaching their own homes; they immediately departed on the run to see to the safety of their families. The mill fire department was obliged to carry on with men whose homes were not in the path of the fire.

Then the wind changed, the conflagration came roaring down on three streets of tenements that adjoined the mill property and the fight was on. The mill firemen used their strong streams to keep the roofs of the factories wet. They carried lines supplied by their big stationary pumps into the tenement area, hitting at the fire as it surged into the flimsy three deckers. But they had to back out of the tenement district.

The men retreated with their streams, taking positions to defend the mill buildings themselves, but when the fire had wholly involved these dozens of tenement houses, the heat was too much for those manning the lines that defended Weave Shed No 6 and some storehouses. They retreated again.

The outside sprinklers on these buildings had been turned on, and water curtains cascaded down the sides of the buildings. Yet, so intense was the heat that the water curtain turned to steam. Then the window glass cracked with the heat and fell out. The fire entered in such volume that the interior sprinklers were overcome.

At this time one of the pumps developed a loose piston rod

and had to be shut down. Mechanics, working feverishly, managed to repair the pump in fifteen minutes. But in the time of reduced pressure, with only one pump working, the fire had taken charge in the other buildings, where sprinklers in the top stories were not getting enough water.

Both pumps were now working at top speed, but the fire had been given fifteen minutes. Firemen cannot afford to give an antagonist such as the Salem fire even so much as one minute. The entire plant was now doomed. The chief of the mill fire department ordered his men to retreat across the bridge over the South River. They left on the double, racing down a street that was afire on both sides.

Six men and E. V. French and Teague remained. They kept steam in the boilers for the pumps in the hope that something might be saved if the sprinklers had water. Earlier, foreseeing this possibility, French had engaged a boat to stand by at the bulkhead at the harbor end of the Naumkeag property.

By ten o'clock the heat and smoke had so increased that breathing was difficult. They stoked the boilers, ran for the boat, and sailed out into Salem harbor, leaving the pumps running at full speed.

These hard-fighting men, battling without any help whatsoever from any of the apparatus from the two dozen fire departments present in Salem this day, were beaten by the well nigh invincible power of the conflagration. True to the tradition of fire fighting, they did not quit while there was one thing more that they could do. And when they left, they saw to it that the pumps were still running.

That was the end of the Salem fire; its arrival at the cold salt water of the harbor. The hundreds of valiant firemen and volunteers had confined it, had held it in a fairly narrow path, yet they had been powerless to stand before it at any point. The Le Favor shoe factory, where a victory was won, was on the edge of the path of flames, not in front of it.

The Naumkeag mills were directly in front of the fire. Here the streams from the two big stationary pumps, the outside sprinklers, the interior sprinklers, all were unequal to the vast heat and power and fury of the invincible conflagration.

Out in the harbor the half-dozen gallant men in the boat, led by E. V. French of the Arkwright, saw the last of it. They watched the flames die down because now there was no more to burn. Then they landed on the far shore and dispersed, to take a hand in the fight at some other point, on one of the sides where the battle was to keep it from spreading laterally. These men were real firemen; they did not go home merely because their job at the Naumkeag was over. Such men do not leave while there remains one more opportunity to swap punches with the fire.

To anyone at all interested in the fire-fighting game, it is instructive to note what Mr. French and Mr. Teague found next day when they entered the burned-out ruins of the Naumkeag. Two buildings had survived the hellish inferno that had swept through the place. Number 10 storehouse had brick walls, an asbestos roof covering, and cornices of metal. There were no windows and only two entrances, both protected by double fire doors. Inside were 1500 bales of cotton, undamaged.

Number 1 storehouse had reinforced concrete walls, roofs, and floors. The windows were small with wired glass in metal sash, protected by tin-clad shutters on the inside, swinging vertically, and held open by a fusible link of metal that melts at a low temperature, thus closing the shutters automatically. The fire did not enter the building, and the finished cotton goods in cases inside were intact. The heat was so intense that the wired glass windows melted, yet the interior shutters prevented the fire from entering.

This conflagration had traveled a mile and a half with almost nothing in the way of fire-resistant construction to halt it. Wooden shingles, wooden buildings, brick buildings with no window protection and wooden interiors; all were swallowed up in the vast sea of flame. Sprinklers, a fire wall, and hard-fighting firemen saved the LeFavor shoe factory. A blank brick wall and strong streams checked the fire on Essex Street, early in its course.

Yet here, at the very end, two really fireproof buildings, carefully engineered, resisted the utmost fury of the fire even after the defenders of the Naumkeag had been obliged to flee for their lives. This is one more lesson in the tremendous part good construction plays in preventing the spread of fire.

What remains to be told is in the nature of footnotes. The militia pitched tents to shelter the homeless, operated field kitchens to feed them and first-aid stations to attend to the injured.

To take the minds of the people away from their woes for a little while, evening band concerts were given by the 8th Regiment Band, the U. S. Marine Corps Band, and the Lynn City Band. On June 29, 1914, the Salem City Council passed an ordinance prohibiting the use of wooden shingles on roofs from thenceforth, proof that this governmental body could learn from experience.

By the next morning the out-of-town firemen were able to

pick up and go home, leaving the guarding of the borders of the fire to the Salem department. At nine in the morning a combination hose and chemical engine and twenty firemen from Cambridge arrived to relieve men who had fought since early afternoon of the previous day; late but welcome assistance. Except for coal piles and a barn full of baled hay that glowed and smoldered for days afterward, the fire was over.

11

The Fight at Fall River

IN 1928 THE OWNERS of the Pocasset Mills in Fall River, Massachusetts, decided that the ancient and enormous six-story stone mill buildings had become obsolete and should be demolished. The wreckers began work early in the year, first removing the plumbing fixtures, piping, and heating equipment, for the metal was high in salvage value. When the plumbing was loaded onto the junkman's trucks, the sprinkler pipes were included.

February 2, 1928, was a cold day, as were most of the other days this crew had been working in the big old mill buildings. Wreckers are a rough and ready lot, with various ingenious ways of making their work less uncomfortable. One of their expedients was a space heater of very simple construction. They placed an empty oil drum on the floor, built a roaring fire of scrap wood in it, and from time to time, when they felt chilled, gathered around it, had a smoke, and told a few stories. Then they would go back to work. When this salamander heater of theirs seemed to be cooling off too much, one of the men would collect an armful of wood and toss it into the oil drum.

On that February day they knocked off at five o'clock, as usual, and went home, leaving their tools where they were to work on the morrow. Also, they left their big salamander, the oil drum, now with a bed of glowing coals a couple of feet deep. It set upon the wooden floor, but this caused no one any concern. Had it not set upon this floor all day? And for several days before? These workmen were not men to worry over much about details.

The part of the big mill building where they were working was not visible from the street. There was no watchman for this group of structures in the process of removal, so there was no one to take note of what happened in the premises of the Pocasset Mills. Later, at 6:27 P.M., to be exact, a police officer passing along the public street outside the group of mill buildings paused to take considerable note of what was happening.

A large volume of heavy smoke was rolling up from somewhere in the mill yard and whipping downwind with the stiff winter breeze. The police officer quite properly concluded that this was a matter not for him to investigate, but for the Fall River Fire Department. He ran to the fire-alarm box and pulled the hook.

Things happened fast in this building of the Pocasset Mills. As the apparatus rolled out of the nearest fire station, about a block distant, they at once encountered a bank of thick smoke. Old hands knew they were on their way to a tough working fire. When they arrived, they quickly laid their lines and got to work.

But the fire had been burning for quite a while. The floors were impregnated with oil from the textile machines which had sat in rows in this old mill for more years than any man could remember. The building had a belt tower, for in an old-time factory the power was transmitted from the engine to the machines by an elaborate system of belts carried from below to the shafts on each floor. These rotating shafts powered the looms and spindles of the textile mill. The sprinklers and their pipes had been hauled off to the junk yard, so there was no protection for these vertical openings running up through the mill. Nor was there protection for horizontal openings, the doorways between one section and another, for the doors themselves had been unhinged and removed.

The fire department had several powerful streams hitting the fire now, with all the first-alarm engines hard at work.

But they were late. The fire racing up the belt tower had now involved all six floors of this old stone building with a wood interior. The good streams the fire department had working tore into the area where the fire was burning when they arrived, yet they could not cope with this entire enormous building now involved in all six stories. Grimly they stood their ground as the chief ordered the second alarm. One more look at the mill, now a mass of flames, and the chief ordered the general alarm, which brought out every piece of apparatus in the city of Fall River.

All of the fire engines in town were not enough for this one. The volume of heat from a building this size is practically irresistible. Within a half hour of the first alarm the fire had spread to the other buildings of the Pocasset group and at seven o'clock they all were burning furiously. The situation was entirely out of hand.

With a stiff wind and nearby buildings of poor construction, the fire jumped the street, attacking unprotected buildings which were soon blazing fiercely. Soon after ordering the general alarm, the chief realized that his department could never hope to control this fire. Immediately he began sending calls for outside aid. Out-of-town apparatus began to arrive at 7:45 P.M. and from then on until midnight they came rolling into Fall River; forty-one fire engines, of which thirty-two were pumps. Twenty-two different municipalities joined in this effort to help sorely beset Fall River.

The longest run was that of three engines and three hose wagons from Boston, fifty miles away. Providence sent four pumps, Brockton and Newport and Swansea and the Naval Training Station sent two each, and the other towns sent one each. Some of the smaller places sent enormous crews with their engines; from ten to thirty men. These were towns with few if any permanent firemen, their reliance being almost wholly upon call men who drop whatever they are doing when the bull whistle atop the town hall blows the number of the box that has been pulled. Many places depend entirely on call men and the apparatus rolls out of the house with some man who lives or works nearby at the wheel. As he drives to the fire, he picks up any call men whom he sees standing at the roadside. The others make their way to the fire on foot or in their own cars, get their rubber coats, helmets, and boots off the kit, and if it is much of a fire, the scene is soon swarming with firemen.

When the big bull whistle blows the signal for an out-of-town call, the men all know this is a real one and put extra speed into their response. One may wonder how it is possible to get thirty or even twenty men onto one piece of fire apparatus. This would be done only in a circus act. The extra men undoubtedly traveled to Fall River in one or more private automobiles and then reported for duty with their engine company.

Of course, no such number was necessary to operate one pumping engine, which these men well knew. They did not pile into private automobiles and hurry to Fall River because they thought their engine was short of manpower. It might be said that they did not think at all. Knowing that a big fire raged in Fall River, they by instinct headed there to fight it. They wanted to be in the fight, as do all true firemen. With them the fight is the thing. Other considerations are secondary.

It may be added that there are occasions when it is very helpful to have twenty or more men on an engine company. If it is decided to run a second or a third line down an alley or through a yard and the engine is already hooked up to a hydrant, it certainly speeds up the operation if a dozen or more men take the hose and manhandle it, on the double, into the spot where it is wanted. And if the men on the nozzle find they are near a wall that is likely to fall or in a spot too hot to stay in, a big crew of men can move the charged line. Otherwise the pipe men would be obliged to shut down and run, with the result that some badly needed hose would be lost by being burned or buried beneath the rubble of a fallen wall.

What makes a study of the Fall River fire particularly interesting is the fact that although the conflagration pattern was well established, defeat was not total. The entire Pocasset

Mill group was burning furiously. A brisk wind was blowing. The terrific heat always resulting from several large structures in flames made ordinary streets no barrier to the conflagration. This one was quite out of hand; entirely beyond the capability of the Fall River fire Department to control. Beyond the business center, where the fire was raging, were residential areas and industrial occupancies with many wooden shingle roofs that had existed before the city enacted its fire resistive shingle ordinance. And in these areas were wooden gutters, porches, stairs, and outbuildings that could easily be ignited by the storm of glowing brands.

This conflagration did not roar across the city and out of town into fields and brush patches. Any true fireman would like to know why this one was not like the others described in these pages that were over only when there was nothing left downwind that would burn. Let us study, one by one, the points of victory. Taken together, they explain the final result.

Across Pocasset Street from the burning mills stood the plant of the Fall River *Daily Herald,* a brick and stone structure with a wooden interior. It was severely exposed to radiated heat from across the street, and its large plate-glass front windows soon cracked and dropped out. Then the automatic sprinklers went to work. Thirty-two heads just inside the windows opened, and a sheet of water came down at each broken window. The fire was halted at this point. Even though the heat was intense enough to burn off a large metal-covered wooden cornice, these thirty-two open sprinkler heads delivered enough water to keep the fire from entering. Three days after the fire, when they had managed to dry out the machines, the plant was running again.

Farther away, on Pocasset Street, was the old building of the Fall River *Herald*. Here, too, the sprinklers opened on front and sides and saved the building. Two buildings in between the old *Herald* building and the new, with no sprinkler protection, were entirely consumed and in the morning only piles of brick and stone remained where they had been. Assisting in the defense of this older building were open sprinklers over the windows, manually operated, which formed water curtains on the outside. Lines from the fire engines were not available at this point, since the fire had become so general that covering every exposure was impossible, but firemen entered the building and used the small hose in the racks in the corridors, thus contributing materially to the defense. This success stopped the further spread of the fire along Pocasset Street.

On Central Street a storehouse of the Pocasset Mills, across the street from the burning main group, was saved by a combination of factors. It was not directly in the path of the wind; it had outside sprinklers on the cornices to provide a water curtain, tin-clad inside shutters, wired glass windows.

Again at the Telephone Exchange, after the fire had burned through two blocks of buildings that were wholly unprotected, built-in features saved the building. Although a fiercely burning frame structure, the Temple Beth-El, was but a few feet away, open sprinklers, wired-glass windows, tin-clad shutters, and fire-department streams on the roof saved the building. So hot was it that the firemen on the roof were forced to retreat, but one crew lashed their playpipe in place so that their stream continued to hit the fire after they had gone down to the street.

At two other points blank brick walls and sprinklers made

stops possible, thus helping to confine the conflagration area. Flying brands started twenty-five fires in the residential areas downwind. Due to prompt transmission of the alarms, out-of-town apparatus covering in at Fall River stations arrived promptly to deal with these, which were mostly roof fires on residences.

Potentially more serious were roof fires on two large mills. When the storm of glowing brands descended onto the wooden towers of the Troy Cotton & Woolen Manufactory, the firemen were all positioned at various points around the six city blocks now ablaze, and the pressure in the city mains was low. As the tower roofs began to burn, a very serious new situation was developing.

Here again built-in fire protection made it possible to prevent a substantial enlargement of the conflagration. The mills had installed a stationary pump capable of delivering one thousand gallons a minute. Mill employees and volunteers carried hose lines to the roof, extinguished the burning towers, and kept the roof wet so that the shower of brands would not start new fires. This mill was only seventy-five feet from the main fire, so this defense was vitally important in preventing the spread of the conflagration.

A half mile east, at Number 1 mill of Merchants Manufacturing, a similar situation occurred. Here, although they lost the entire roof of one tower, the powerful streams of the mill's stationary pump protected the long, old-fashioned mansard roof of the mill, a type of construction which ignites readily if showered with wind-borne burning brands.

The end came in the block of buildings across Bedford Street from the Troy Mills. This was the sixth city block to become involved, an area of frame buildings that were old and very combustible. No one acquainted with fire protection would have thought this group of buildings a very good spot for defense against an onward marching conflagration.

However, it so happened that here most of the Fall River engines and the thirty-two out-of-town engines had concentrated. The report written by the conservative National Fire Protection Association states that here among these fire traps there was "remarkable work on the part of the firemen," and there is a reference to "massed fire apparatus."

Anyone familiar with fire fighting can imagine the scene as the men from the majority of the forty pumping engines waded into the battle with two and three streams from each. Large-stream appliances and single lines with all the pressure the hard-working engines could give them met the conflagration head on.

The firemen deluged these frame buildings along Rock Street and broke the intense heat. Their left flank was protected by the Troy Mill, well wet down by the men handling the lines supplied by the big stationary pump. Their right flank was protected by the fire resistive courthouse building. This battle was fought on a narrow front because the successes at a number of buildings having some degree of protection had prevented the fire from spreading sideways. Thus it was possible to meet the conflagration head-on with massed streams; an unusual concentration from the apparatus of twenty-three communities.

The battle was won; victory in a head-on battle with a conflagration, something rarely achieved. But there was one notable defeat; an episode from which something can be learned.

Four blocks from the point of the fire's origin, on the corner of Purchase and Bedford streets, stood the Buffington Building, a five-story, first-class building with brick walls and a steel and concrete interior. In its rear, which was the side toward the fire, were wired glass windows in metal sash. The combustible building in its rear was consumed, but the wired glass windows of the Buffington Building held.

Either by burning brands or radiated heat, or both, the fire crossed Purchase Street and soon the entire block of buildings on the side of the street opposite the Buffington Building was fiercely burning. In the front of this building were plain glass windows instead of wired glass windows. The heat radiating against the wind from the burning buildings across the street struck the plain glass windows, the glass cracked and dropped out, the radiated heat now reached the contents, and soon the entire interior of the building was ablaze.

Everything in the four stories above the first was completely burned out; all furniture, supplies, and merchandise on hand were as completely gone as if they had never existed. Yet the windows on the first floor held, because they did not receive as intense heat. It is well known that heat rises. Therefore, it was the upper floors that received the most intense heat; it was the windows on the upper floors that failed and admitted the fire.

One lesson here is that wired-glass windows and metal sash are required on all sides of a building, including the front, since heat from across an ordinary street is enough to break a plain glass window and ignite the contents. The second lesson is demonstrated by the condition of the Buffington Building after the fire. The windows and the contents were gone, but the integrity of the building was unimpaired.

Workmen applied a new skim coat of plaster to the walls,

painted, installed new windows, and the structure was again ready for occupancy. This showed the strength of a first-class steel and concrete building under the most severe conditions imaginable.

The Fall River fire started and became so powerful that a conflagration was inevitable because of two adverse factors. One was a stiff wind. The other was a group of enormous and highly combustible structures from which had been removed their most essential protection; automatic sprinklers and fire-doors.

This fire could have leveled a major part of the city. It was confined to six blocks and halted because of a combination of favorable factors. It is worthwhile to list here the factors which prevented this one from equaling the disasters at Salem and Chelsea and many other places.

1. An excellent water supply was available at all times.

2. The system of outside aid worked perfectly. From twenty-two other municipalities came thirty-two motor pumpers and nine other pieces, mostly hose wagons, with a total of 348 firemen. These came at request, with no delay or attempts to evade this call to heavy duty. And they came at speed. This is all in the tradition of fire fighting. When such a call comes there is only one question: How soon can we "get in there?"

3. Standard hose couplings. Every city had the same couplings, a lesson learned after the Baltimore fire in 1904 when much of the out-of-town apparatus was badly delayed in getting to work because their hose couplings did not fit Baltimore hydrants. The National Fire Protection Association led the movement to make hose couplings standard throughout the country.

4. A reliable fire-alarm system. When brands set fires a half mile or more away, a box pulled in that neighborhood transmitted accurately the location of the outbreak.

5. Numerous buildings with built-in fire protection. Firewalls, automatic sprinklers in the interior, open sprinklers on the outside, wired-glass windows and metal sash, steel and concrete interior construction, racks of small hose in the corridors, in two instances large stationary pumps in the buildings of a design approved by the Underwriters, metal-clad shutters—all combined to help the firemen check and narrow down the conflagration at various points.

At the end the final blow was struck by the massed concentration of streams from most of the forty engines at the fire. This was a glorious experience for the firemen who were present that night; the final showdown, a toe-to-toe fight with the biggest fire any of them had ever seen, streams that were straight with the pressure from the hard-working pumping engines behind them, straight streams that hit hard into the roaring flames and at last blackened more and more of the area of these burning buildings. Then the moment when it was clear this fire was knocked down and some of the men could be sent to get a sandwich and a cup of hot coffee, while the others shifted from one burning spot to another, drenching the last of the flames. The men, heartened by the hot coffee, returned to relieve those on the playpipes so they, too, could go out to the trucks with the big urns and paper cups and sandwiches and apple pie.

So it gradually ended. Out-of-town companies picked up ice-covered hose and went home. Fall River posted lines at places still smoldering. It was over except for the visits of the insurance men and the writing of reports.

12

Some Tough Ones

THE FIRES we have described are the big ones; the classic disasters of our era. There have been many other fires that got away, smaller ones for the most part. Seaside resorts are frequent victims of sweeping fires. Boardwalks, frame hamburg joints, wooden roller-coaster arrangements, little hotels, and close crowded summer cottages have the makings of a conflagration. Coney Island, Nantasket, Revere Beach, Atlantic City, all have seen some wild times when fire became master for a while.

Back in steamer days, a church encampment in a lovely pine grove, where the small wooden buildings were close together for greater fellowship, had a sudden introduction to the more worldly aspects of life. The elders who governed this group had never thought of the desirability of a water system and hydrants. Drinking water was romantically ob-

tory and defeat at certain points in the battle to keep the fire from widening. When every able-bodied person is doing everything he can, the cumulative effect is tremendous.

This day there were men with garden hoses, tea kettles, pans, and buckets everywhere, alert to douse burning brands as they fell. One house on Broad Street was saved, although it caught fire six times, because there was a man on the roof using receptacles of water passed up to him. There he stayed through it all, taking buckets and pans of water and soaking the roof as the hail of glowing embers fell upon it. This man astride the ridge pole and his sweating helpers who formed a line to pass pails and kettles and even chamber pots up to him won out, for when the main fire at last passed on, the house still stood. When he finally decided it was safe to edge down over the wet roof, which was smeared with the charcoal of the embers he had doused, his shirt was half-burned off his back and his face was streaked with soot. But the lady of the house was happy to set before him a glass of cold ginger ale and a huge slice of her best cake.

Other volunteers were helping to solve the shortage of cannel coal. Salem's supply of fuel had never been calculated to take care of two dozen hard-working steamers, and the fuel wagon was having its troubles getting about with what coal they had. The bystanders turned to, scavenging neighborhoods for wood to throw into the ravening maws of the fireboxes of the steamers. One group of high-school boys who had come over from Lynn adopted one engine as their own, ranging far and wide in their search for picket fences. They broke these up and stacked the pieces within reach of the stoker, who thus was able to keep up a full head of steam for his engine.

ing the line at a distinguished old three-story mansion of the Federalist type of architecture, thus preventing the fire from working eastward along this thoroughfare of fine old houses. Here the fire-fighters had an excellent assist; a blank brick wall on the west end (the fire end) of the building. Whether the man who built this house around 1800 ordered the blank brick wall because he was over a century ahead of his time in the matter of fire safety or because he did not fancy his neighbors on the west side, we do not know. But we do know that here was an excellent stop.

One may today see this old mansion which was the easterly fire limit on Essex Street. It is plainly in the old style, the buildings west of it are of the style of 1914, since they were erected to replace the houses burned in the big fire.

In this part of Salem, in the path of the fire, are the west ends of some very distinguished streets; Essex, Chestnut, Warren and Broad, all composed mostly of the mansions of the old Salem merchants of the very early part of the nineteenth century. These streets are visited every year by thousands from all over the country, who come to admire the distinction and beauty of these remarkable early American houses.

Of Chestnut Street, the great historian Samuel Eliot Morison has said, "Architecturally it is the most perfect street in North America." This fact the firefighters well knew and so did the people of Salem. The firemen and countless volunteers struggled desperately to prevent the fire from spreading sideways down these streets.

It appears again and again in the accounts of these major conflagrations that the work of citizen volunteers was of immense value, sometimes spelling the difference between vic-

work beneath piazzas. They nestled into the angles of porches and barns and hen houses and found lodgment in lumber piles and anything wooden in yards or near houses.

As if a major conflagration were not enough for the sorely beset city of Salem to endure, another fire started in North Salem, three quarters of a mile from the main fire. This area was not to leeward, or down wind from the main fire, so it could not have been set by sparks and burning brands. This one started from some one of the dozens of causes of fire.

When the alarm for the fire in North Salem came in, there was the immediate problem of finding apparatus to respond. Out-of-town companies handled it, and when the firemen finally arrived, they found a serious fire in progress, one which might easily assume conflagration proportions. They fought a desperate battle, and halted the fire after losing ten houses and two barns. At one time twenty buildings were afire.

This North Salem fire did not become a conflagration for the reason that the firemen got ahead of it and were able to face it. In this struggle there was a factor of extreme importance. Steamers and hose wagons from Lawrence had arrived by rail not long before and were sent directly to the fire. On Hose 5 was a deck gun capable of receiving three lines.

The engine lines were coupled onto this deck gun and from its big, long nozzle came one stream; straight, powerful, delivering a thousand gallons a minute and with tremendous hitting power. This stream, supplied by two hard-working steamers, ripped into the fire. Fragrants of boards and shingles flew about wherever the stream struck, and the pressure carried the water into every part of these burning structures.

The stream from Hose 5 of Lawrence and the other lesser streams halted this fire and most of the apparatus was able to leave and join the fight against the main fire. It should be carefully noted here what this deck gun, a large-stream appliance, accomplished. A large stream has the reach to get water onto a real hot fire, whereas a hand line with its shorter reach may not permit the men to get close enough.

A large stream gives volume of water and power, and the power is important in subduing a bad fire. Firemen say they "knocked down" the fire when they have managed to get it under control. This expression is meaningful. There is something about the hitting power of a heavy stream that adds effectiveness.

The story of the North Salem fire, a bad fire in itself, is relatively pleasant reading, because it is a story of victory. The boys beat that one.

As for the main fire, the conflagration, there is no need to recite its ghastly progress across town, street by street. Some statistics, briefly stated, will serve to outline the magnitude of the disaster. The area burned was 253 acres, 1376 buildings were leveled, the devastated district was a mile and a half long and a half mile wide. The loss was $15,000,000. Twenty thousand people were left homeless, and ten thousand became unemployed because of the destruction of the factories in which they worked.

In this recital of the defeat of the firefighters at so many stages of this struggle, it helps to be able to find, here and there instances of victory. The places where the firemen won were, of course, at the sides of the fire as they fought to keep it from spreading sideways, widening, broadening its path.

On Essex Street, near Pine Street, they succeeded in hold-

tained by going to a well with the old oaken bucket. Toilets were a modern notion not present here; small wooden edifices out among the pines served and were satisfactory except when the wind was from a quarter that left the encampment to leeward of this row of structures.

One breezy summer day a fire started in a cottage and could not be controlled by the bucket brigade of campers. When the town fire department arrived, their chemical tanks were soon exhausted and their steamer could find no place from which to draft nearer than a pond a half mile away. There was not that much hose available.

By this time a half dozen of the little wooden cottages were burning, the glowing brands were blowing downwind, and the situation was wholly beyond control. The chief of the local department could not think of any worthwhile next step, but at least he did something. He sent calls for aid to a dozen nearby communities, asking them to send all available chemical engines.

This was quite an order in those days, for every community had at least one chemical or combination and some had four or five. So the result was that a couple of dozen chemicals were soon speeding toward the old camp ground. The firemen managed to save some of the buildings that were not in the crowded area, these structures were vulnerable to the burning brands that showered down on them and these the chemicals saved. They narrowed the fire down some by working at the edges, so the end result was that some of the little cottages still stood when it was all over.

Today the chemical engine is a thing of the past, but something better has taken its place; the booster tank. These contain as much as three hundred gallons of water, which is much more than a large chemical engine's capacity. These tanks are carried on an ordinary pumper or ladder truck. Another type, carried on a tank truck, sometimes contains as much as a thousand gallons of water.

Apparatus with a water tank can get a quick refill at any hydrant, pond, or well or it can keep going if a bucket brigade is pouring water in at the top. The chemical tank, when empty, had to be recharged with sulphuric acide and bicarbonate of soda, as well as water. When the spare supplies of these chemicals were gone, this apparatus was useless until it returned to quarters to obtain more soda and acid.

In any such discussion as this, the same question is always asked. Under modern conditions, can there be such conflagrations as those described in the preceding chapters?

The answer to this is a regretful affirmative.

Within the last few years an outstanding expert on fire protection and fire hazards wrote an article in which he discussed a dozen American cities in which a conflagration could occur. These communities all have entire districts closely built with frame structures of considerable size; multiple occupancies commonly known as tenement houses and sometimes termed three deckers.

In these cities the fire departments and water systems are, for the most part, excellent. Yet with a combination of unfavorable circumstances, a fire could get beyond control.

The unfavorable combination of circumstances that could result in a major conflagration is composed of elements familiar to all of us. It is not necessary that all occur in a given situation. Should some occur, the seeds of disaster are there. It is worth while to enumerate here the various unfavorable factors several of which can combine to produce a conflagration.

1. An area of closely built wooden buildings.

2. Wooden shingle roofs.

3. A strong wind blowing at a rate of twenty miles an hour or more.

4. A large building with inflammable contents, lacking automatic sprinklers and located near other buildings not provided with sprinklers, metal-clad shutters, or wired-glass windows and not of first-class steel and concrete construction with firewalls and fireproof doors.

5. A delayed fire alarm or delayed discovery.

6. A weak fire department or a situation where an important amount of fire apparatus is engaged elsewhere.

7. An insufficient water supply or some happening that partially disables the water mains.

There are favorable factors today that were lacking when most of the conflagrations we have described took place. Again, for the sake of brevity these should be listed.

1. The many painful lessons of the past have convinced municipal governments that wooden shingle roofs are an inexcusable menace. Ordinances forbidding them have existed in most communities for so long that nearly all wooden shingle roofs have now been replaced.

2. Modern motor fire engines are able to respond more quickly than the horse drawn apparatus or the cumbersome motor tractors that were attached to the steam fire engines. For response to boxes near at hand there is little difference in running time, but for the longer runs made by apparatus responding to extra alarms from fire stations farther away the

time difference is important. For the response of fire engines coming from other towns under mutual-aid arrangements, the greater speed makes a great difference in assembling fire companies to fight a serious blaze.

3. In the last few decades the amount of fire-fighting equipment in most municipalities has increased markedly. A chief has much more to work with today. Particularly is this true in small towns that formerly relied on a couple of chemicals and now have a water system and three or four good pumps and are able to send an engine company to assist another community that is hard pressed. It comes as a surprise sometimes to see at a serious fire in a big city pieces of apparatus from various small towns.

4. Mutual aid has had a tremendous development. Today's arrangements provide for covering in at empty fire stations by apparatus from nearby towns so that there is a response to another alarm even when the entire department is at work on a serious fire. It is up to the chief in command to decide which out-of-town engines cover in and which go to work at the fire.

With the development of fire-department radio, a large part of a county may be under a central control station that dispatches enough fire apparatus to meet whatever situation exists. For instance, practically all of Cape Cod is united in one system. Should a serious fire threaten the business area of any town on the Cape or one of the large hotels, fire engines all the way from Provincetown on the east to the towns near the canal on the west would be on the move at high speed over modern superhighways to the point of danger.

5. More attention is being paid each year to built-in safety factors such as automatic sprinklers, wired-glass windows,

blank brick walls, and first-class steel and concrete construction. This means more structures in which a bad fire will not originate and more structures that will resist the progress of a sweeping fire and give the firemen another opportunity to make a stand.

An instance of this is a half-mile district of three deckers and other closely crowded wooden dwellings where one entire city block has been demolished under an Urban Redevelopment project and two old-age housing units have been built. These new buildings are of steel and concrete, all floors are concrete, stairways are wholly of incombustible materials, all steel beams are encased in concrete. The two buildings are surrounded by wide lawns.

This entire district has been a worry to the underwriters for a half century; it is marked on their maps as one of the places where a conflagration is most likely to occur. Today there are still plenty of nests of three deckers so close together that there is not room to drive a motorcar between them, old barns, junk yards, blocks of stores and taverns.

Yet if a fire should get out of control, here is one spot where the fire department can make a real stand, for the new buildings are like fortresses standing in the way of the onward sweep of the flames. The open lawns around these buildings are wide enough to diminish the heat before it reaches ordinary buildings in the block beyond the project; perhaps sufficiently diminished so as not to be capable of transmitting fire.

Here we have taken a quick survey of dangerous conditions, and of improvements that we hope will make a general conflagration less likely. Now let us have a look at a few tough ones.

At Fall River in 1927, the makings were there. Under slightly different circumstances this one could have burned right out of town to die out in the bushes at the outskirts. Modern motor apparatus racing over the roads from considerable distances—the Boston kit came over fifty miles—made possible the massing of over forty powerful streams at the point where victory was won. And several stops at various points were possible because of modern built-in protection; automatic sprinklers, wired-glass windows, blank walls, and metal-clad shutters. Fire-resistive roofs on many houses and independent mill fire pumps were of great assistance in controlling this terrific blaze at Fall River.

At Nashua, New Hampshire, on May 4, 1930, it was a different story. This town had not caught up with one of the most important modern ideas for fire protection; namely, fire-resistive roofs. There was no municipal ordinance requiring the use of fire-resistive shingles. Unfortunate Nashua collected the reward of this folly.

As in Baltimore, this fire, at first appeared to be a small working fire easily handled by the first-alarm assignment. Two wooden railroad trestles, side by side, carried tracks of the Boston & Maine Railroad over the Nashua River. The bridges were two hundred feet long, each supported by three latticed wooden trusses, roofed with wooden sheathing and the sides boxed in with sheathing. Thus each bridge was like a tunnel made of wood. The space between the bridges was another enclosed area because of the overhang of the two sheathed bridge roofs.

These two bridges were ideal for protecting the tracks from the deep snows of a New Hampshire winter. It is probably that no one had ever carefully considered the possibility of what did happen to these two structures on a bright, breezy Sunday in May.

It is not known how fire started in the under part of one of these bridges, nor is it very important how it started. Bad fires wreak their destruction rarely because of the way in which the fire originated but because of construction that is in defiance of the principles of fire safety and unfavorable circumstances such as high wind, delayed discovery, weak water supply, and failure of fire-fighting efforts due to accident or weakness. Fires start from one of a multitude of causes. Man must prepare to meet fires he knows will start in some way. Good construction, alertness, strong fire departments, and adequate water supplies are the answer. Good luck counts. So, too, does a strong fighting spirit in fire department and citizenry.

A cigarette butt tossed aside may have started this one. So may boys playing with matches or a rat gnawing on the head of a wooden kitchen match or a person of mental aberration who fancied it would be sport to watch a fire. A pedestrian saw smoke rising from the bridge and sent in an alarm from a nearby street box.

Luck entered into this situation; bad luck. The firemen ran a booster line to deal with this seemingly insignificant fire. They found they were not reaching the seat of the fire because the sheathing deflected the stream. The fire was increasing, so they ran a big line, then a second one. Another alarm ordered by the chief from a box on the other side of the bridge brought a second alarm assignment and the men at the nearby Jackson Mills ran two lines.

Even with a half dozen good streams in action the fire continued to increase and build up heat. Protected by walls of sheathing that kept the water from reaching the flames, it became a veritable volcano. Flames fed by great quantities of dry wood now swept up through the bridge structure and roared to a height of seventy-five feet.

Borne by a stiff wind, burning brands from the fiercely burning bridges were carried to leeward by the countless thousands. Everywhere downwind in this city that had not yet learned of fire-resistive shingles these glowing coals fell on bone-dry roofs, rolled down the slopes, and collected in the valleys and the gutters.

In a fire of this type, red hot coals gather in the valley between the roof and a gable until there is a glowing mass. When this happens the entire top of the house is soon ablaze, unless a fire engine appears to put a strong stream on it. At such times there are usually no fire engines. They are busy elsewhere.

Not only do the shingle roofs ignite, but dry piazza floors, stairways, lattice work beneath the porches, fences, hen coops, any lumber or baskets or boxes in the yards are likely to catch from the storm of brands. There is fire everywhere, spreading without anyone to check it.

Downwind, to leeward, swept the burning brands from the blazing bridges into a district mostly residential, showering the wooden shingle roofs. Every dwelling that caught fire added to the volume of sparks pouring across the city. The fire was now entirely out of hand, the chief realized, and he began calling for out-of-town help. Each shingle roof fire soon involved the entire building and each burning building gave off intense radiated heat that involved one or more structures near it. This sequence occurred so frequently that the fire was progressing through the entire district. No longer was this a number of houses set afire by burning brands. It was a conflagration, enormous, inexorable, consuming all in its path.

Here and there a victory was won. A number of houses with fire-resistive roofs were saved even although standing in the fire area, but others with fire-resistive roofs were so near other burning structures that their walls were ignited and they were overwhelmed by the conflagration. A fireproof roof plus a good stream from a fire engine usually was the winning combination.

A victory was won at the McElwain shoe factory group. Here brick buildings of one and two stories, with ribbed window glass in metal sash and automatic sprinklers, resisted the fierce heat from the burning frame buildings of the nearby Nashua Building Company. However, victories were few that day.

One dreadful menace was narrowly averted by quick thinking. In the Crown Hill section stood the Infant Jesus Roman Catholic Church where in the parochial school hall six hundred children were watching a play. As the fire came toward the church, some excitable idiot rushed into the hall and yelled "Fire."

Here was the immediate danger of panic, which experienced firemen dread above all things. Immediately a priest leaped to his feet and shouted for attention. The children, who knew this voice of authority, listened. The priest then announced that there was a fire in the neighborhood and if they would obey the commands of the sisters and march out in an orderly way, they would be dismissed and be allowed to go watch the fire.

The children calmly filed out, shepherded by the sisters,

and not long after the last of them were out of the building, the onrushing conflagration attacked one corner of the church. It was soon entirely involved and in another hour was no more than a ruin. But the level-headed priest had seen to it that six hundred children in his charge, his flock indeed, were safely off the premises before the conflagration reached the building.

The fire burned right out of town, leveling houses, barns, garages, lumber yards, an ice-cream-freezer plant, a cooperage plant, stores, and churches. The fire ended in the woods. Across the Merrimack River in the town of Hudson, the burning brands set fire to a house and a garage and set a forest fire which destroyed fifteen acres of woodland before it was checked.

Out-of-town apparatus began to arrive in Nashua at 2:35 P.M., a little more than a half hour after the first alarm, and continued to reach the scene from then until 9:45 P.M., when engines from towns in the suburbs of Boston arrived. The longest runs were made by the companies from Winchester and Belmont and Arlington in Massachusetts, which roared thirty-two miles over the roads to help a sister community in its hour of disaster.

Some of the out-of-town kit was very adequately manned. Merrimack sent twenty men with its pump, Milford thirty with its two pumps, and Chelmsford thirty-five with its two pieces that responded. Several others arrived with ten- and twelve-man companies.

It should not be assumed that these towns maintained regular crews of any such strength. Indeed, most of these departments were mostly if not entirely call men. When the whistle blew the out-of-town call on this bright Sunday in May, any-

The fight to save Old South Church in the great Boston fire. Streams of tremendous power kept the steeple wet and extinguished fires in the belfry.

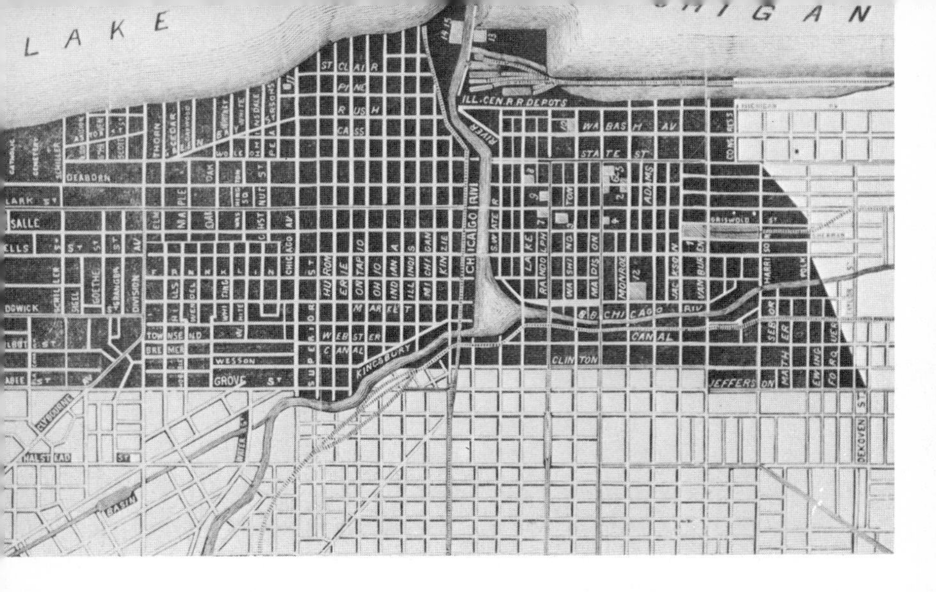

The burned district in the great Chicago fire. Dekoven Street, where the cow kicked over the lamp, is at lower right of blackened area. *Below:* An artist's recollection of a scene at the Chicago fire as burning brands and the vast heat of the conflagration carried the fire across the Chicago River.

National Fire Protection Association

A photograph of the ruins after the San Francisco earthquake and fire.

Salem Public Library

Margin Street, Salem fire. Everything beyond this house is burning. If they stop the fire here it will be a victory even though the house is a ruin.

Broad and Hawthorn Streets, Salem fire. Two steamers in the successful fight to keep the conflagration from working into an area of beautiful old homes.

Salem Public Library

Joseph E. Scanlon, Jr.

Deck guns at work on a fourth-floor fire in a factory making celluloid novelties. Prompt concentration of large streams held the fire in the fourth floor.

Joseph E. Scanlon, Jr., photo by Alton Hall Blackington

Church fires are likely to be total. This was a cellar fire when the apparatus arrived, but the lath and plaster walls had no fire stops.

Harold S. Walker Collection

The massive and powerful streams of a fire boat's nozzles hit a coal-wharf blaze.

Benjamin Ellis

Critical moments in a Boston three-decker fire. The right side of the street is burning furiously and radiated heat has ignited the houses across the street.

Joseph E. Scanlon, Jr., photo by Alton Hall Blackington

Harold S. Walker Collection

Above: After the fire. Interior of a five-story lodging house with brick walls, wooden interior, no sprinklers, and an open central stairway. Twenty tenants were fatalities. *Left:* Firemen battling a blaze in an older type of school with a wooden interior and pitched roof.

Benjamin Ellis

Touch and go whether this fire in a group of three deckers will become a conflagration. The firemen have one strong line where at least six are needed.

Joseph E. Scanlon, Jr.

In demolishing this old factory workmen carefully removed the sprinklers and pipes. Wreckers then cut up machinery with acetylene torches. The result was this hot fire.

Harold S. Walker Collection

A study in power. Two deck guns and a water tower at work. The aerial ladder is ready for the time when men can take handlines into the upper floors.

Harold S. Walker Collection

Action. A strong engine line at work, and men carrying in dry hose for another. *Below:* A strong engine line needs more than two men. These two are having difficulty, as the stream shows.

Harold S. Walker Collection

National Fire Protection Association

The Sherry Netherlands fire in New York City was wholly beyond the reach of the fire department because the building's fire-fighting equipment had not been installed.

New York City Fire Department

Two of the five units of the Superpumper. *Above:* Drafting through a twelve-inch suction hose. *Below:* The deck gun of this tender can literally knock down a building.

New York City Fire Department

one who is familiar with the game knows that every man with legs to carry him would head straight for the fire station. The three hundred firemen and many volunteers with forty pieces of apparatus put up a valiant battle. They never did check the fire, but they did manage to keep it to a narrow path. Thus did they save most of the city. And no one who fought at Nashua on that Sunday early in May will ever forget this tough one.

A list of fires of conflagration proportions since 1900 occupies six pages of fine print. To give a detailed description of each, such as the accounts we have given in the preceding pages, would require a tremendous volume. Tough ones have occurred in all parts of the United States and Canada. Jacksonville, Florida, lost 1700 buildings in 1901. Paterson, New Jersey, lost 525 buildings in 1902. In 1904 Toronto had a $13,000,000 blaze in the business district that destroyed 104 structures. In 1911 the New York Fire Department had a wild time at Coney Island, losing two hundred of the crowded resort buildings. As we have said, the list is long. The destruction ranges from thirty buildings in some places to one thousand at New Bern, North Carolina, in 1922. In each of these the group of unfavorable elements making it possible for the fire to get away are not unusual. The villains in each fire drama are two or more from the list we already know so well.

To conclude on a note of optimism we will mention a couple of tough ones that developed with unbelievable rapidity and yet were controlled before becoming conflagrations. The first of these was in Lynn, Massachusetts, a factory city with a population of 92,000 that has experienced periods of industrial growth when large numbers of new people moved in to work in the shoe factories or the plant making electrical machinery. These growth periods came at a time when neither builders nor the city regulatory authorities understood as much about fire safety as is known today.

So anything went in those days; wooden shingle roofs, three deckers so close there was not room between them to swing a cat by the tail. Crowded into the yards were the cottage houses that had stood at the front of the lot before the landowner mortgaged the place to raise money to build the three- and six-family houses that now were at the front of the lot. This situation is not a peculiarity of Lynn; it is typical of the American factory city, except that in New England the three-deckers are almost always of wood.

At three on a Sunday afternoon in November, with almost no wind, we were driving a motorcar when we heard fire apparatus approaching on an intersecting street. We halted until they emerged and then followed at a respectful distance. This was first-alarm apparatus, but when we turned into the street upon which the fire was located we could see, three blocks distant, that the street was so full of smoke it was impossible to see beyond.

We parked the car two blocks away and ran to the scene. One block distant was a fire station quartering a thousand-gallon pumping engine. On the corner was a fire-alarm box. It was Sunday afternoon in a thickly populated area with people on the street who could see the fire and pull the box.

Yet the entire rear of a long three-decker housing twelve families was burning fiercely. A pitched-roof two-and-a-half-story dwelling next door was burning, and across a narrow driveway three more three deckers had caught. These were smaller buildings, housing three families each. In this driveway, when we arrived, was the crew of the engine from the station nearest the fire, manning a hydrant line which they were switching back and forth in a desperate effort to halt the progress of the fire.

All five of these buildings were burning and this hydrant line was the only water on the fire. The apparatus we had followed in was at this moment laying a line and so was the third engine company scheduled to respond to the box. Why, one might ask, did they lay a hydrant line to a fire of this magnitude? For the sake of speed. They got water much quicker by hooking up a line to one of the hydrants than if they had attached the engine's suction pipe to the hydrant and then had attached their line to the pump and had waited for the operator to start the pump. Minutes saved at the very start of a fire are of tremendous importance.

As this crew switched their line back and forth in the driveway, the glass in the windows of the smaller three deckers was expanding with the radiated heat from the fiercely burning larger building. The glass cracked and dropped out. The heat ignited the lace curtains and furnishings and soon the rooms were a mass of swirling flames.

We turned back to see what the engine was doing. It was at the hydrant. When the hydrant line was laid, the men had put gates (valves) on both of the two-and-a-half-inch outlets. To one of these they had attached their hydrant line. Now the operator had finished attaching one of his suction pipes, a two-and-a-half-inch soft suction, to the gate on the other side of the hydrant.

A ladder company, satisfied that all the people were safely out of these buildings, speedily pulled hose from the body of the engine, attached it to one of the outlets of the pump, and carried the dry hose down the driveway on the run. We watched them down there in the narrow, smoke-filled driveway, luridly illuminated by the rolling flames, as they screwed on the long brass nozzle or playpipe.

From these laddermen came a hand signal to the pump operator and the cry "Water" echoed down the narrow passageway. The operator, who had stood at the driveway entrance awaiting the word, now dashed to his pump, shifted his lever, and accelerated his motor. The water came. The limp, flat hose filled out and became round, and the hose moved with the life in it and was symmetrically curved.

At the nozzle the water spit and coughed for a few seconds, the stream arching feebly ahead to fall on the pavement. Then the motor began to roar deeply, and the arched stream became a straight, clear, hard column that tore into the blazing three decker with mighty power. Wherever it struck, this engine line blackened the fire and tossed half-burned fragments of wood and pieces of charcoal every which way.

Now the men at the playpipe of the hydrant line shut down. One of them ran back to the engine to help the operator disconnect from the outlet on the hydrant and connect to the pump. Then the man ran back to take his position on the big brass nozzle, the operator notched his throttle ahead, the roar of the motor became deeper and heavier, and another strong, straight line tore into the blazing three deckers.

We watched the operator's next move. He took another short soft suction, connected one end to the gate from which the hydrant line had just been removed and connected the other end to one of the two intakes of his pump. Now he was sure he would have plenty of water to work with. This is a "quick hitch" arrangement enabling the engine to get into action more swiftly. It is more correct to use the big black rubber hard section to connect to the big four-inch gate on the hydrant, sometimes termed the steamer gate.

But to connect the big suction, two men are required. It is a fussy and exacting job to line up the threads of the suction and the threads of the steamer gate. If there is reasonable pressure at the hydrant, the soft suction will serve. If the hydrant pressure is weak, then the pump is likely to collapse the soft suction and the operator will wish he had taken the time to fit the hard suction to the big gate. When drafting from a pond, well, or river, the hard suction must always be used.

Sometimes the operator can get enough water for two or even three lines from only one two-and-a-half-inch suction. To do this requires good pressure at the hydrant. There was good pressure in this area, but this operator, looking over his shoulder, saw the second alarm apparatus rolling in and by the look of this fire he knew there would be more alarms. Then the water pressure, with many engines drawing on the mains, would be increasingly uncertain. The third alarm, which was sounded over the big whistle on the gas house, was blowing now, summoning more apparatus and the off shift of every company now at the fire or on the way.

Hardly had the two rounds of the third alarm echoed off into the distance than the big gas house whistle commenced to bellow again. This was the general alarm, what the firemen call ten blows. That is what it is; ten blasts, repeated once, summons every remaining piece of fire apparatus in the city and one engine company from nearby Swampscott. These five blazing buildings required everything that the general alarm calls for and perhaps more.

The situation now hung in the balance. Was the fire going

to get away? To leeward was a half-mile district of crowded dwellings, three deckers, houses in the yards, stores, junk yards; an area well known to the fire Underwriters and marked with heavy crayon on their maps. We walked around to the other side of the fire to see how it looked there. We were just in time to become involved.

Engine 4's men were working a strong line. One of the crew had managed, with help from volunteers, to drag in a second line of hose. It lay there on the ground, dry and flat and limp, as this fireman screwed on the big brass playpipe.

The man was an optimist, a person of great faith. He shouted "Water" in a bull-like bellow, grasping the brass nozzle with firm grip. Holding an engine line is, of course, beyond the strength of any one man except Hercules himself. Then the fireman shouted to the bystanders, "Give me a hand."

We stepped forward and so did one other and thus was this fireman's optimism justified. The water came. The hose rounded and became a living thing. We soon had a straight stream aimed into the blazing kitchen on the third floor of the big three decker. The kitchen was an inferno of solid flame as we stood on the ground in the back yard and directed the stream through the rear window, moving it just enough to wash the ceiling of the room.

Seldom have we had the opportunity to feel so powerful. Gradually the orange flames darkened here and there, more smoke came from the place, some of the water from the line soaked down into the floor below, the fire began to diminish perceptibly. We were wearing our Sunday suit and next day it had to be sent to the cleaners for a real treatment. But it was worth it.

A fireman from the off shift, attired in rubber coat, helmet, and rubber boots, was nudging us now. We finally got the impression he thought he was the one who should be helping to hold that brass playpipe. Reluctantly we surrendered it and drew back three paces, dripping, to watch.

This fire had one of the conflagration elements, a large body of fire with intense heat. However, the other unfavorable factors were not present. There was little wind. There were few wooden shingle roofs to leeward, for the city had long had an ordinance forbidding them.

The water supply was good, the fire department alert, powerful, and trained to hit hard and fast. In the front of the building two deck guns, each with three lines running into it, were directing massive streams into the fire.

So they knocked it down. No buildings became involved that were not already involved when the fire department arrived. To be able to say this is to pay a high compliment to the work of any fire department.

Inevitably comes the question: How did this fire gain such a headway in the middle of a Sunday afternoon with a fire station only a block away and a fire-alarm box on the corner?

One answer may be this. Nothing makes a quicker or fiercer blaze than the back piazzas of a three decker. They are lightly built, with light floor boards and ballisters, and on each piazza is usually a collection of objects the tenant considers valuable. Here a tenant may be keeping some empty cardboard cartons that might come in handy some day, a couple of wicker rocking chairs for a summer evening, a few wooden boxes in which to grow flowers or perhaps radishes.

And the back piazza is a very handy place to keep a drum of fuel oil for the kitchen range. It saves a trip to the back yard or cellar to fill the glass bottle that fits in back of the stove and it eliminates the possibility that some neighbor may get confused and help himself at one's oil drum.

So boys who build a fire beneath the first floor piazza to cook some hot dogs, or a cellar fire, or a drunk who falls asleep in one of those wicker rocking chairs and lets his cigarette drop on a cushion, or a fire in one of the kitchens can easily get the back piazzas going. Unless the discovery is very prompt, the entire rear of the building and perhaps other buildings will be involved when the first-alarm apparatus arrives; the kind of fire where the District Chief in charge says "Give me the second" to his driver before he even gets out of his car.

We recall one afternoon when we were industriously working on some difficult documents in our office in State Street, Boston. As far as fire apparatus goes, State Street is a crossroads. If there is a big one anywhere in town, the fire engines responding to extra alarms go by in groups, with intervals of a few minutes between. When they are rolling in this rhythm, it is time to find out what is happening.

On this afternoon, a call to the Boston *Globe's* city room produced this information; that they had a five-alarm fire in East Boston. The documents were laid aside, a taxi took us through the Sumner Tunnel and into the closely built residential area that lies well back from the wharves of the East Boston waterfront. There, hard at work, was the major part of Boston's Fire Department, plus engine companies from Chelsea, Revere, Malden, Everett, and Lynn.

The fire was in a row of three-family houses, ten of them. And the developer who built them a generation ago had not wasted a square foot of space. They stood snugly near each other in an example of togetherness that would give any fire-protection engineer bad dreams.

Of these ten buildings eight were burning. Here, again, was a situation that might easily have got out of hand and assumed the conflagration pattern. Some of the elements were there; a big fire, intense heat, a closely built community of wooden buildings with no protection against exposure to fire, no blank brick walls, fire doors, wired-glass windows, or sprinklers, not even a garden hose for a resident to use.

But there was not a conflagration that day. There was little wind, no wooden shingle roofs, and there was prompt discovery and a massive response of fire apparatus that surrounded this one and drenched it. Although, we lost no time getting over there in the taxi cab, the fire was knocked down by the time of our arrival. The eight three deckers were all total losses; gaunt ruins that had to be removed.

Twenty-four families were homeless. Here, again, was an example of what happens when fire becomes established in the rear piazzas of this type of structure.

We were told the story of a fire of a somewhat similar nature in a three decker. In a small Massachusetts city, the department, responding to a box alarm, found the second floor involved in three different places. There was a brisk blaze in the front room, or parlor, another and separate fire in the middle, or dining room, and another fire in the kitchen was "going pretty good," to use the fireman's phrase.

Some quick work with the ladders and one-and-a-half-inch lines quelled these fires. In the back yard was the mattress of a studio couch, burning smokily, so they extinguished that as well. This was a peculiar situation; four separate fires, three in the building and one in the yard.

The efforts of the firemen to understand this one met with some success when they discovered a man on the rear piazza, asleep in a rocking chair. There he had been during all the commotion that attends the arrival of the apparatus and the putting out of a fire. None of this had disturbed his slumbers.

The firemen had trouble waking him. From the strong odor of liquor emanating from his person, they decided that unusual methods were required, so they turned the stream from a one-and-a-half-inch line on him.

This was successful. He wakened with bursts of volcanic profanity. The man holding the nozzle of the small line managed to calm him by suggesting that another dash of city water might be a good idea.

Then the firemen got enough information from this rapidly sobering fellow to piece together the order of events. After having had a few drinks, the man lay down on the couch in the parlor, peacefully puffing on a cigarette. He dozed. He dreamed it was a hot day, and awoke to discover that he was surrounded by fire from the burning chintz couch cover.

Being a man of action, he leaped to his feet, seized the mattress of the couch, and dragged it across the room, across the dining room, across the kitchen, and out onto the back porch. Then he hove the burning mattress overboard and sank into a chair to enjoy a well-earned rest. Soon he was asleep again.

The burning mattress had ignited the rug in the parlor and some magazines in a rack. It had started a lace tablecloth in the dining room and yesterday's newspaper and a straw-bottomed chair. In the kitchen, it got the wastebasket going and a carton of groceries.

Of these events he was completely unaware. The police, when he had told all he could recall, took him in charge. He got a ride downtown and lodgings in a small room of a less combustible nature. If this episode teaches a lesson, it is doubtless that it is very unwise to smoke in bed.

13

Skyscraper Fires

WHEN AMERICAN ENGINEERS, architects, businessmen, and financiers combined their capabilities and ambitions to produce the type of building that came to be known as a skyscraper, they needed various other experts to help them. One of these was the fire-protection specialist.

It takes little imagination to picture the ghastly and spectacular disaster that would result if a building of twenty, thirty, forty or more stories were to have a serious fire. Such a structure is beyond the reach of the streams from any water tower. No aerial ladder in existence can go beyond the tenth story. No mortal can jump into a landing net from an upper story of even a moderately high building with the slightest hope of surviving. The impact would force the net to the pavement and reduce a human body to a lifeless thing.

So the very best efforts of the most capable engineers in

every field have combined to make the American skyscraper fire-safe in every way. Their work has been remarkably successful. Over the years serious fires have been almost nonexistent in this type of building. The few that have occurred serve to remind everyone of the strict principles of fire protection that absolutely must be observed at all times.

The fire in the Sherry Netherlands Hotel in New York on the evening of April 13, 1927, is a classic example of what can happen when some of the principles of fire protection in skyscrapers are forgotten for even a short while. This thirty-eight-story building was under construction, but the exterior was nearly completed except for the upper part of the tower, where a large amount of wooden scaffolding was still in place. On the outside of this new skyscraper were the wooden structures of two elevators used to hoist building materials to the floors where needed.

Design for the fire protection of tall buildings calls for a complete system of standpipes rising vertically and serving each floor. These standpipes are fed by water pumped into them by fire engines which connect up to the Siamese intakes on the outside of the building at street level. One may observe on the outside of every high-rise building the double, or Siamese, intake pipes.

The standpipes are also fed by water tanks well spaced and in the upper stories of the building. The Sherry Netherlands Hotel had water tanks at the twelfth and twenty-third floors and one in the tower, intended to contain water pumped into them by big stationary pumps in the basement. At each floor the standpipes had hose connections. In case of fire, the firemen would go to the floor upon which the fire was located, using an elevator to reach the floor and to carry their hose.

The pressure of the water from the tanks and pumping engines should combine to give the firemen good working lines from the standpipes to which they connect. The Sherry Netherlands had two eight-inch standpipes installed, one of them extending to the tower.

However, the standpipe to the tower had not yet had its cap screwed on. Therefore, water pumped into this standpipe with pressure enough to reach the thirty-eighth floor ran over the uncapped top of the standpipe. The tank in the tower had not been connected, had no water in it, and was of no use in this situation. A cross connection between the two standpipes on the twenty-second floor had not yet been installed.

This was the situation of the interior fire-protection system of the building when at quarter of eight on April 13, 1927, as the spring twilight was deepening, people on the street noticed a fire in the wooden scaffolding on the thirty-eighth floor, very near the top of the building. A policeman pulled the box, thus sending in the first of five alarms.

With the arrival of the fire department the operators of the pumping engines connected their hose lines to the Siamese intakes at street level. The hosemen went to the floor where the fire was with their hose, and connected to the standpipe. They got no water. Then it was that the firemen discovered that the cross connection at the twenty-second floor had not been installed, the cap for the top of the standpipe was not there, and the tank in the tower contained no water.

A hasty attempt by the firemen to insert a piece of pipe at the twenty-second floor to complete the cross connection was unsuccessful. Even had this improvisation worked well, there is doubt among the experts whether the pumping engines New York then had could have developed the three hundred pounds per square inch necessary to get water to that height. And with the pressure they did have many lengths of the hose leading to the Siamese connections burst.

So here was complete frustration and failure. Water flowed from the cross connection at the twenty-second floor. Water flowed from the uncapped top of the standpipe. The men who had connected their hose lines to the standpipe at the floor where the fire was located got no workable streams to fight this furious fire fed by wooden scaffolding and various building supplies. There was little they could do. The fire burned as freely as a barn in a remote country community. Not a line was put on the fire as it enveloped the top of this lofty building, providing New Yorkers with a stupendous spectacle such as they had never expected to see.

Burning boards and timbers from the scaffolding dropped constantly to the street, leaving fiery trails in the night and sending up showers of sparks when they struck the pavement. Brands streamed off to leeward over the city, and the clouds of smoke were illumined by the flames of the blazing tower. Photographers, amateur and professional, here had the picture opportunity of a lifetime.

This fire ran its course, blazing all night without being checked at all by anything a well-nigh helpless fire department could do. No water tower or aerial ladder pipe could reach it, no water was in the standpipes with which to battle it. It burned until there was nothing left to burn and it went out when no more fuel remained, as does an upcountry barn when nothing is left but the cellar.

When the fire was over, the lower part of the Sherry Netherlands Hotel was not damaged. The exterior of the upper part was blackened and spalled, the elevator machinery was ruined, the wooden scaffolding was gone, steel beams not yet protected by concrete fireproofing were buckled and warped and so worthless they had to be replaced. All building materials on hand were consumed and the neighboring buildings had suffered some damage from the burning timbers that fell constantly during the height of the fire.

It was a frustrating lesson, for the best fire department in the world accomplished no more than a volunteer company from a country town with its chemical and mongrel pump. And an expensive lesson, for the damage to this uncompleted yet superb building took a half million dollars to repair.

Here are the things that were learned and written into the book for the guidance of the future.

1. Scaffolding should not be of wood. Today we see very cleverly developed steel scaffolding.

2. In a building under construction, with lumber, paint cans, and other combustible material lying about and primitive heaters improvised by workmen to keep warm, there must be fire-fighting equipment ready for instant use. Recommended are hand extinguishers, a forty-gallon chemical tank on wheels, portable water pumps such as are used by the Navy and by forest fire units. If made possible by the progress of pipe installations, a line of hose connected to the water supply is best of all.

3. During construction an enclosed elevator in a fire-resistive smoke tower should be in operation so firemen and their hose may be carried swiftly to the location of the fire. For firemen to be obliged to drag hose up twenty or more flights of stairs is an undeserved penance.

4. Workable standpipes, tanks, and stationary pumps at all stages of construction must be available for the fire depart-

ment. The lack of such installations at this fire made a farce of the fire department's efforts to control the blaze. Strict inspection at frequent intervals is necessary to see that all fire-fighting equipment is connected. The episode of an uncapped standpipe was inexcusable.

Another New York skyscraper figured in a lurid fire drama, this one a stark tragedy. The Sherry Netherlands fire was a tremendous spectacle, yet there was no loss of life. The Empire State Building fire counted fourteen dead. Dismal as was this fact, it was some satisfaction that the disaster was in no way due to the failure of fire-protection measures.

The Empire State Building is one of the world's greatest engineering accomplishments, towering 1472 feet into the sky with a 222-foot television sending tower on top. As with all of New York's tall buildings, extraordinary efforts made it as fire safe as the principles of fire-protection science allow. It was fire-resistive in the fullest meaning of this technical term used by fire-protection engineers.

A fire-resistive building has masonry or reinforced concrete walls, a frame of reinforced concrete or steel encased in concrete. It has no naked steel members. The floors, roof, and interior partitions are of material that will not burn and are sufficiently protected so that they will not give way or fail under great heat. The Empire State Building met these requirements.

For active fire fighting it had nine eight-inch standpipe risers, two of them going as high as the eighty-third floor. On these many floors were racks of two-and-a-half-inch hose connected to the standpipe risers. The total length of hose ready for immediate use was over six miles. To step up the city water pressure there was in the sub-basement a stationary pump of 750 gallons a minute capacity, other such pumps on the twentieth, forty-first, and sixty-second floors and a 280-gallons-per-minute pump on the eighty-fifth floor. An enormous water-supply tank of ten thousand gallons capacity was positioned in the sub-basement, and five-thousand-gallon tanks were on the twenty-first, forty-second, and sixty-third floors and a thirty-five-hundred-gallon tank was located on the eighty-fifth floor.

The New York Fire Department had pumping engines capable of developing a pressure of six hundred pounds per square inch, acquired after the Sherry-Netherlands fire, to deliver water into the Siamese connections at street level of every tall building. These connections are for the purpose of enabling engines to pump into the building's standpipes so that firemen working on the floors above will have effective streams. From 1931, when it was built, until 1945, the Empire State Building's life had been uneventful, from a fire-protection viewpoint. What fires there had been were localized and easily handled by this superb equipment.

Then on July 28, 1945, came the moment when all fire-protection measures were put to a most exacting test. On this misty morning an Army B-25 two-engine bomber approaching New York was advised by radio to land at La Guardia field. The pilot for some reason decided to head for Newark. There is a standing order for all aircraft to maintain at least a two thousand-foot altitude over Manhattan. This plane was much lower.

Visibility was two and a half miles, which to an earth-bound mortal seems a great deal. An airplane at 250 miles an hour covers that distance in forty-five seconds, so that is the time in which the pilot must execute a maneuver to go around whatever large object he seeks to avoid; a mountain or—the Empire State Building.

This pilot did not execute in time. At 9:52 A.M. his bomber struck the Empire State Building with a thunderous crash at the seventy-eighth and seventy-ninth floors, tearing a hole in the north wall eighteen by twenty feet. The three-man crew were killed instantly. The body of the plane plunged into the seventy-eighth floor, fortunately empty except for paint cans stored there by the building employees.

Flaming gasoline sprayed over the building for five stories above and five stories below the point of contact and set fire to the stored paint on the seventy-eighth floor. On the seventy-ninth floor women clerks in a charitable agency received the full force of the burning gasoline and eleven were fatally burned. One of the motors demolished an elevator shaft and a fire tower surrounding a stairway. Flying debris cut the cables on an elevator and the operator had the terrifying experience of an unchecked descent of seventy-eight stories. He lived to tell of it, but his injuries were serious.

Parts of the flaming plane went across the inside of the building, through a window, across West 33rd Street and descended to strike a penthouse atop a twelve-story building on the other side of the street. This started a fire in that building which caused damage of $75,000. This fire activated automatic sprinklers and set off a fire alarm which registered in fire headquarters. An alarm from a street box was pulled at about the same time.

Four alarms were sounded within eight minutes. Twenty-three engine and ladder companies responded and when they arrived they found three distinct fires. One fire was in the seventy-eighth and seventy-ninth stories where the plane had struck 913 feet above the street. Another was in the lower part of the elevator shafts, caused by burning debris that dropped down the shafts from the fire above. The third fire was across the street where flaming fragments of the plane had descended upon the penthouse on top of the twelfth floor of the building there.

In this fire everything worked as it should. Although the fire was started under the most unfavorable circumstances, a large quantity of flaming gasoline, the structure of the building resisted the intense heat as it was intended to do. To the Siamese intakes on the front of the building the New York Fire Department connected lines from pumping engines that can deliver water at six hundred pounds pressure per square inch. At the seat of the fire on the seventy-eighth and seventy-ninth floors crews of firemen went to work with strong water lines. Other crews hit the fire at the bottom of the elevator shafts and still others extinguished the fire in the penthouse and top floors of the building on 33rd Street. There they were aided by automatic sprinklers. A total of twelve lines were used.

One standpipe was ruptured by flying wreckage, yet this created no problem, for a cross connection with another standpipe carried the flow of water. The fire was extinguished promptly because this was a truly fire-resistive building with excellent interior fire-fighting facilities. It is a marked contrast with the Sherry Netherlands fire, where so many acts of omission resulted in a situation where the fire department had little to work with.

This test showed the excellence of the engineering work that went into the Empire State Building and the care taken to keep everything in working order. Here, again, the damage was $500,000. Yet it is interesting to note that only 20 percent of this damage was caused by the fire. The rest of the damage was caused by the massive blow of the plane that stove in so much of one side of the building.

On January 9, 1963, the Empire State Building had another fire that started in a pipe shaft carrying various pipes and cables upward through the structure. The insulation on a pipe through which chilled water ran was of a combustible material. This fire was intermittent between the twentieth and the sixty-seventh floors, which is a situation familiar to any one who has had to fight a partition fire in an ordinary frame house. Such a fire has to be chased from one point to another.

The fire started at 4:35 A.M. When people began to arrive for work in the offices, the fire department was still struggling with this intermittent fire, which seemed to be in hand. The chief decided it was safe to permit this vast throng of people to enter the building, go to their various offices, and get started on the day's work. This he found to be a mistake.

Some of these hundreds of people did go to their desks and get to work. Many others hung around to watch the firemen work out their baffling problem. Some complained about the smoke with the expectation that the fire officials could do something about it if only they felt like it. Still others, probably call men in some volunteer fire department way out in the suburbs, offered all manner of advice to the firemen as to dealing with this stubborn blaze. When their suggestions were not adopted they extended the opinion that the New York Fire Department was stupid.

The important point about this stubborn blaze is that it never was out of control for the reason that the fire department was trained for work on a skyscraper problem and all the built-in fire-protection features functioned as they should.

Two other high rise or skyscraper fires are sadder chapters.

One of these was the Astoria Building in Rio de Janeiro, Brazil, June 28, 1963. On the fourteenth floor of this twenty-two-story fire-resistive building a fire started in a film-developing laboratory. An employee went to fetch a fire extinguisher to deal with a burning plywood backer to a screen upon which they were projecting.

It is well known that there are few worse places for a fire than in a place handling photographic film. When the man returned with the extinguisher, the entire office was involved. The flames swept into the hall and thence into an unenclosed stairwell, which acted like a chimney.

Fortunately the building fire alarm was sounded promptly, thus permitting many of those on the floors above the fourteenth to escape by way of the elevators before the fire became general. But a great many on the upper floors did not leave in time, with the result that they were trapped.

A heroic chapter was written here when the trapped people broke down the brick wall separating the Astoria Building from the hotel next door and made their escape by that route. Others escaped by ladders and ropes run across from nearby buildings. Two occupants fell from ladders or ropes while using this escape route and were killed. Two others perished in the building, the total death list being four.

The standpipe failed to give sufficient water to permit the firemen to make a fight of this one. It was discovered later that the valve on the tank on the twenty-second floor was closed. The Astoria Building was erected in 1916, which gives rise to the thought that its construction may have failed to embody many of the principles of modern fire-resistive construction.

Certainly an open stairwell is a grave defect and a water tank with a closed valve is worthless. So severe was the fire in the upper stories that the government ordered that all of the building above the thirteenth floor be rebuilt.

In Atlanta, Georgia, on December 7, 1946, at the fifteen-story Winecoff Hotel occurred one of the most ghastly of the fires in high-rise buildings. This was a good steel and concrete fire-resistive building. But a number of rules evolved over the years and well proven by experience were ignored. The stairway was open, when it should have been enclosed by fire-resistive materials. The doors were of wood. The transoms over the doors to the rooms were open. The furniture was of combustible material. The partitions in the halls and corridors were covered with painted burlap. The trim was of wood. There were no automatic sprinklers.

In this fire 119 people died and ninety were injured. Some may ask, "How did it start?" That question is not useful. Fire can start from many common causes that are always with us. The proper question is, "Why did it spread?" Four entire floors were wholly involved; a fiery furnace in which no man could live. And the answers are at hand; the answers are right there in the last half-dozen sentences of the previous paragraph.

Let us here give a word of warning to those who may see somewhere in their daily travels conditions which they recognize as having the makings of disaster by fire. Anyone who learns even a few of the principles of fire safety will somewhere see these principles violated. Should you speak out if you see dangerous conditions? Be warned that if you do speak out, you will be considered an odd ball, a queer character who is perhaps touched in the head, or perhaps you will simply be told to mind your own business.

Should you, then, hold your peace if you see conditions you know to be dangerous? That question we cannot answer for you. It requires a different kind of courage than that which sustains a man as he rushes into a burning building to attempt a rescue or works on the tip of an aerial ladder in swirling smoke and heat, wondering when the wall may give way and come over on him. But the courage to speak up is a very valuable kind of courage. It might save more lives than a whole ladder company getting in there on the first alarm for a tenement-house fire with people hanging out of the windows.

There is no knowing when or where any one of us may encounter conditions we know to be dangerous. It may be a blocked fire escape, a locked exit door, plans for a new building or alterations that include inflammable materials in a hallway or failure to provide sprinklers in a stairwell. Or someone taking liberties with gasoline. The list is long. Do you speak out or do you see to it that you do not get involved. We cannot answer for you. But so much does depend on alert and observant and courageous citizens.

Another illustration of fires in high-rise buildings occurred in a structure not nearly as well along toward completion as the Sherry Netherlands Hotel. Fully as many of the rules of fire safety were violated; some of the same ones and a few different ones. On the rising ground above Scollay Square,

Boston, in the late autumn of 1938, the new Suffolk County Court House was nearing completion. Standing adjacent to the old granite, mansard-roofed Court House, it stood twenty stories; a new landmark for the flat Boston skyline in those days broken only by the Custom House Tower.

The concrete floors and brick outside walls were already in place on the lower floors. In the upper part the steel workers were still busy. Plank floors laid on the girders gave them a footing and a place for the furnaces in which they heated the rivets. Boxes and crates of supplies were stacked here and there. At some points big tarpaulins were hung to protect the brick masons on the curtain walls from the piercing cold winds of late autumn. Straw was on hand, plenty of it, to protect newly laid mortar from a sudden freeze.

In the late afternoon, as the light faded, we sometimes paused in Pemberton Square, in front of both courthouses, to watch the work. It was quite a sight. Cranes hoisting steel I beams and loads of brick and buckets of concrete; high in the building the riveters and bursts of staccato hammering as the air guns pounded red-hot rivets into place.

The man who heated the rivet took it from the furnace with tongs and tossed it to a man who held a bucket. The rivet made a fiery arc through the air in the dusk, disappeared in the bucket, then reappeared for a moment, glowing redly. Thrust into a hole in the steel it threw off sparks as the pneumatic hammer struck its burst of rapid blows to pound into place another part of this towering and majectic structure.

Not always did the man with the bucket catch the red-hot rivet that was tossed to him. When he missed it, the rivet fell, its fiery trail making a long, graceful downward curve until it was out of sight somewhere in the work below. Occasionally the long downward curve was interrupted when the rivet struck an I beam and bounced off in a new curve and perhaps struck again to make still another curve. Eventually a rivet that was dropped passed out of sight somewhere lower down where the tarpaulin windbreaks were hung to protect the bricklayers.

More interesting than desk work, we mused, turning away to return to the office. One afternoon we stood with another man who also had paused while on an outside errand. We both watched a descending rivet describe an extra arc after striking a beam. He grinned as he turned to me.

"It won't be long now," he said.

We did not know the gentleman, but we knew exactly what he meant. And it did happen one afternoon about a week later when we happened to be in a town a dozen miles away on business. So we missed all of this very expensive spectacle, a five-alarm fire that had everything.

Whether it was a red-hot rivet, a cigarette, a coal from a furnace, a poor electrical connection, or spontaneous ignition did not appear. Certainly the frequent descent of the red-hot rivets entitle that cause to first consideration. But we have said before that what starts a bad fire is not as important as what makes it spread. It is what makes it spread that makes it bad; not whether it was a cigarette or a delinquent boy with matches or lightning that started it.

It spread because there was straw and scrap lumber and crates and cartons lying about and tarpaulins hanging at the sides. It spread because the temporary floors were of wood and because half-empty paint cans, with the covers off, stood about. It spread on wooden elevator shafts, and the gasoline for the hoisting engines helped.

There were no fire-fighting appliances on the site of work at all capable of dealing with a substantial fire. Then, when the fire department got in there, they discovered that the standpipes were not capped. Instead of going up into the half-finished building and connecting hose to standpipe outlets, the firemen had to drag hose up stairways from the street level or over ladders.

New Yorkers, when the Sherry Netherlands burned, were presented with a remarkable spectacle such as few who watch fires or fight fires ever see. So were the Bostonians. The Court House fire burned into the hours of darkness. The blaze was visible in the suburbs and out to sea. The tarpaulins blazed and dropped off, the planks and boxes and cartons and piled lumber burned brightly and were finally wholly consumed. The firemen got water onto parts of the building and got the fire out in such spots as they could reach with hand lines, aerial ladders, and water towers.

Finally it was all over and there remained the steel frame and the brickwork and the concrete floors and a tremendous uproar from the public. As usual, the public wished to know how this fire in the New Court House of which they were so proud had started. Had this been ascertained, the public would have been somewhat satisfied. And if whoever could be in any way blamed for the start of the fire could have been sent to jail, the public would have been considerably more satisfied.

The Court House has been completed all these years now and many a dramatic legal battle has taken place in its various oak-paneled court rooms. Yet at no time has there been here any performance more dramatic than the battle of the Boston firemen with a fire burning from twelve to twenty stories above the street in materials such as might be found in an ill-kept carpenter shop. And they fought without a stand-pipe to give them water. No firemen, in Boston or elsewhere, ever give up, no matter what the handicaps. So the Boston boys did all they could, and some of this fire they put out, but some if just burned out.

14

Loss-of-Life Fires

Most firemen come to think of their work as more than a mere job. To them it is a calling, a profession that requires all a man has to give. And what he is required to give may be a very great deal. So often at a serious fire we see the ambulance leave the scene, headed for the hospital with siren wide open. In it may be a fireman who has stepped on a nail or has been cut by falling glass, or perhaps two or three who have had too much smoke.

Usually the men who get such a ride are treated at the hospital and released. But if it is a fracture case, a long time will pass before the fireman is on the kit when it rolls out of the house. Very occasionally, if a wall has collapsed or if the dreaded back draught has done its wicked work, there is a man in the ambulance for whom the last recall has sounded.

The battle with fire, ever varied, is a challenge to every fire-fighter; a challenge to which they respond gladly and with alacrity. Fire-fighting is a contest, a game with a tough adversary, a contest the true fireman loves. The one exception is a fire that involves loss of life. These they hate and dread. Taking people out over the ladders or leading them out through the smoke is not unusual, but, fortunately, taking out bodies in the long wire basket with which every ladder truck is provided is a rare occurrence.

In a medium-sized industrial city some years ago a man whom we know was getting up one morning when he heard the outside whistle blowing the second alarm for a box located on the other side of town. The third alarm soon followed and then the general alarm, calling out every fire company in the city. He could hear the bells and the sirens of the fire apparatus in his part of the city as they responded. Later, after breakfast, he walked down town. On his way he met the fire engines from his part of town returning, the coils of wet hose stacked on top of the hose body of each. What he particularly noticed was the expressions on the faces of the firemen; grim, set, and sad. Later in the day, when he saw in an extra edition of a newspaper that twenty people had been killed in a furious blaze in a chemical plant, he was not surprised. The faces of the firemen had told the story of disaster. One look at them on the returning apparatus was enough to tell him that here were men who had seen death.

A fireman told us of the night they responded in the small hours to an alarm from a box near their quarters. The fire was in a four-story apartment house and the firemen, as their apparatus rolled out of the station, could hear the cries for help from the victims trapped in their rooms. There was quick work with ladders and landing nets, with many rescues. But the building was extensively involved when the fire department arrived. Fragments of burning wood were dropping off, and a fireman with a hand chemical had to stand by to douse flaming embers as they fell on the landing nets. Five of the residents did not make it.

Firemen do not like this part of their work. Nor do we like to write this chapter. Yet it is necessary. It is only as more and more intelligent citizens become alert to hazards that we can hope for fewer disasters. So, with this preface, we will proceed to tell the stories of some typical fires involving loss of life.

The Triangle Shirtwaist Company in 1911 occupied the eighth, ninth, and tenth floors of the Asch Building at Greene Street and Washington Place in New York City. Here women worked on sewing machines turning out hundreds of shirtwaists. The machines were close together, and cloth scraps and tissue paper littered the floor. Here and there about the premises were rag bins, and finished blouses hung on lines.

At quarter of five on March 25, 1911, a fire started in a rag bin on the eighth floor, jumped to a long table piled with cotton cloth, and ran along the table. There were fire buckets, but no one emptied one onto the fire in time. Hose lines were attached to standpipes, but they had not been tested for a long time. The valves had rusted closed, and no one was able to turn on the water and get a stream on the fire.

The building had an elevator which would take twelve at a time. Some escaped by using it. There were two stairways with doors opening inward. One was jammed shut by panic-stricken people who pushed against it in a mad rush to escape the flaming room. The door to the other stairway was locked. Workers, piling up against it, could not open it and were caught by the flames.

There was a fire escape on the outside of the building so

steep and narrow it accommodated only a few. On the tenth floor many girls went up to the roof, from which they made their escape by a short ladder some New York University students in the next building found and put in position for them so they could climb the short distance to safety on the roof of the adjoining structure.

Many made it, but the dreadful toll was 146 dead and 70 injured. Some perished by burns or smoke asphyxiation in the burning shirtwaist shop. Some jumped from ninth-floor windows to the landing nets of the firemen on the street below, but no landing net can check the velocity of a body that falls that distance. One who jumps from the fourth floor may survive, but the inexorable fact that velocity increases as the square of the distance obviously decreases the chance of survival of those who jump from greater heights. The chance of survival decreases with every foot added to the height of the jump. A point is reached where the person is falling at such velocity that the net cannot possibly check the fall. The net gives in spite of the efforts of the men holding it and the person strikes the pavement and suffers a mortal blow.

The lessons from this ghastly episode were clear.

1. A door opening inward in a place where a large number of people assemble is a death trap.

2. Constant vigilance is required to see that someone does not lock exit doors. Locking a door makes it easier to keep track of the goings and comings of workers and others.

3. Fire-fighting equipment should be carefully inspected periodically to see that it is in working order. In this fire rusted valves rendered useless the hoselines in the building. A good stream early in the fire could have saved lives.

4. The building was of good construction and was struc-

turally sound after this fierce and deadly fire, but the inflammable contents burned and the death list was long. Automatic sprinklers are the one answer to inflammable contents. Many persons are deluded by the notion that a serious fire cannot occur in a first-class fire-resistive building. It can. Photographs of the interior of the Triangle Shop show wooden tables and chairs not completely burned. The fire department put the fire out before the contents were wholly consumed. Yet there was a hot fire in there long enough to result in 146 deaths.

To all who are interested in fire safety we make this suggestion. When you see an exit door in a place where many people assemble, try it to see if it opens. To any one who berates you for doing this, it might be stated that it would be very easy to let the State Fire Marshal, or a similar authority, pass on the question of whether or not you are a meddlesome busybody.

The Triangle Shirtwaist fire occasioned great public indignation. In a funeral procession eighty thousand people marched in the rain behind an empty hearse drawn by six white horses. Public meetings, editorials, and sermons on the disaster were numerous.

It is unfortunate that such a great price must be paid for public improvements, yet much of our progress is gained the hard way. As a result of this tragedy the legislature established the New York State Factory Investigating Commission. Within their jurisdiction came not only fire safety, but sanitation, ventilation, occupational diseases, and home work in various phases of manufacturing. Many remedial laws resulted and the enforcement of existing laws became much stricter.

Yet even today someone in charge often thinks convenience will be served by locking an important exit door. It is easy to test them and it might save lives.

Schoolhouses present serious problems in the protection of life. On March 4, 1908, the Lakeview School in Collinwood, Ohio, burned with the loss of 173 pupils and two teachers. The first cause was a building of poor construction. It was of wood and only the walls were brick. A door from the cellar opened into the first-floor corridor so that a fire starting in the cellar quickly filled the corridor with smoke and flame. The stairways were open and soon were blocked by fire and smoke.

The second cause was panic. Some children fell in the vestibule near the rear doors. Others fell over them and a jam was created, even though the doors opened outward. The panic occurred in spite of fire drills.

The value of stairways enclosed in fireproof materials was more generally recognized after the Collinwood fire. Such stairways are not cut off by fire and smoke. First-class construction, automatic sprinklers, and enclosed stairways are the only answers to a disaster such as this one.

In the years since the Collinwood school fire there have been many improvements in schoolhouse construction. Many of today's schools are of one or two stories, of first-class construction, and have fireproof "smoke towers" or enclosed stairways. The worst disaster of recent years, that at the school in New London, Texas, on March 18, 1937, was an explosion of natural gas rather than a fire.

Some theater fires have cost many lives. The classic disaster of this kind occurred in the ill-famed Iroquois Theatre in Chicago on December 30, 1903. Poor construction, insufficient exits and, above all, panic were the factors causing the loss of 602 lives. Many were trampled to death. Since that time improved exits, better construction, inside fire-fighting equipment, a fireman in uniform on duty during performances, an asbestos curtain and, in many instances, automatic sprinklers have all combined to make today's theaters much safer.

Tenement houses, sometimes known by the more genteel term apartment houses, vary considerably as to fire safety. The wooden three-decker so common in industrial cities, where they are often crowded together in groups, can make a very smart fire. Nothing burns more merrily than the back piazzas of a three-decker. And a group of them always has the potentiality of a general alarm fire.

Yet the ordinary three-decker is not a serious life hazard, because it usually has back piazzas and front piazzas. If a fire starts in the cellar, which is common, and comes up the open back stairway, also common, the occupants can go out on the front piazza and await the arrival of the ladder company. If the fire originates in the front of the building, which is less usual, and involves the open front stairway, the tenants can go to the rear piazza and await rescue.

The life hazard exists in apartment or lodging houses of greater height, usually having no piazzas, front or rear. A fire in the cellar or a lower floor charges the open stairway with smoke and hot gas. Usually there is an elevator, which gives another vertical area in which heat and smoke can collect. A tenant who becomes alarmed, opens a door, and goes out into the hall may be doomed, for the smoke and hot gas are lethal.

If an alarm is not sent in promptly, the mass of gas is likely to ignite, making the center of the building a volcano of fire.

When the fire apparatus arrives it is touch and go whether the firemen, assisted by police and bystanders, can get the people out. We remember one such fire where three lives were lost. The fire originated in the cellar, traveled up the stairwell, and turned the top part of the five-story building into an inferno. And yet the windows on the first floor were not broken. The fire sought a vertical opening and bypassed the first floor.

At that time we sought legislation to require sprinklers in cellars, stairways, and hallways of multiple occupancies. The legislation did not pass. Everything went along in a calm and usual way for years. Then Lady Luck in a mean mood came forth with another cellar fire in the still watches of the night. This one was also in a five-story structure of small apartments, with an open wooden stairway, a wooden interior, and no fire protection at all. By the time the first piece of apparatus pulled up in front of the building, the occupants were hanging out of the windows.

There was a second alarm, a third, and then the general alarm, each one minute after the other. There was fast work with aerial ladders. The landing nets were snatched off the trucks and opened up. A ring of firemen, policemen, and citizens held each net, desperately maneuvering to be under each body that hurtled down from the upper stories.

Some missed the net, some made a good landing. The first engine company in, instead of doing rescue work, hurried to stretch a hydrant line through the front door to hit the fire roaring up the stairway. Their plan was to give the occupants on the upper floors more of a chance by reducing the volume of fire surging upward toward them. One of these firemen told us that as he walked across the sidewalk to shout the signal to the man at the hydrant to give his crew the water, a body hit the pavement one foot in front of him.

One more stride and this firemen would have been an ambulance case, to say the least. The person who jumped was too panic stricken when the fire worked into his room to wait for a ladder or for the maneuvering of the landing net. So he took one desperate leap into eternity.

It was a very bad night. The result of the fire, in a building the ignorant thought safe because it had brick walls, was a body count of twenty. Some of the tenants had never waked up. They simply drifted off into the next world when the smoke got them. The rear of the building was on an alley so narrow the ladder company on that side could not do much and they lost some there. And a five-story jump into a landing net does not always have perfect results.

Twenty bodies made more of an impression than three bodies. The legislation requiring automatic sprinklers went through, fast.

All the loss-of-life fires we have described occurred in typical occupancies: a garment factory in a tall building, a school, a theater, tenement and lodging houses. From them have evolved new laws and safeguards. The last of such fires we will describe was in a very unusual place, not at all typical; indeed, there probably is not another place like it in this country. It is to be hoped there is not.

The Cocoanut Grove night club in Boston occupied a very substantial fire-resistive reinforced-concrete building once used as a garage. The owners had made very much of a success of it. The interior décor simulated a tropic isle, with cocoanut palms, fronded leaves, and other tropical verdure in liberal quantities. These leaves and trees and cocoanuts were all made of cloth and paper fashioned by skillful hands.

The concrete walls and ceilings of this fortress-like garage were not at all a romantic setting, so the night-club planner concealed them with plywood and wallboard on light wooden frames. The Cocoanut Grove had a cocktail bar in the basement called the Melody Lounge. There was also a regular bar, a dance floor, a dining room, and another cocktail lounge at street level.

The Boston authorities had given the Grove an official seating capacity of 650. On Saturday evening, November 28, 1942, about a thousand guests were there having the usual after-game parties following the Boston College–Holy Cross football contest. An employee in the basement Melody Lounge tried to replace an electric light bulb in a fixture set in one of the artificial palm trees, and the better to see what he was doing he lighted a match. Witnesses state that he blew the match out when he was through and put the match stick in his pocket. Other evidence indicates that this match ignited the palm tree and still other evidence indicates that faulty electric wiring started the fire.

As the report of fire-protection experts states, the exact source of the ignition was of less importance than the fact of insufficient exits and inflammable decorations. However the palm tree caught fire, the indisputable fact is that in seconds the crowded Melody Lounge was involved in one of the most peculiar fires ever recorded in the history of the subject.

Fire was seen along the wall near the floor at the same time as in the branches of the palm tree. Flames traveled along the ceiling. The decorations, the artificial leather on the walls, and the cloth-covered ceilings burned rapidly. Some said the flames seemed to roll through the air rather than to spread along the surface of the ceiling. With the fire was thick, heavy black smoke which seemed to have a poisonous and noxious quality.

The fire crossed the Melody Lounge and went up the stairway toward the main entrance. Immediately Cocoanut Grove was in desperate trouble. The first grim scene was a panic-stricken rush to get out of the basement cocktail establishment. The crowd rushed for the stairway. Most of them made it, but a few did not. The rescue workers found some bodies there after the fire and, strangely enough, some who still lived. A few escaped from the basement by going through a small cellar window. Some went into the kitchen, and a few others found safety in a large walk-in refrigerator.

The great majority who stormed up the stairs found that a door on the first floor that opened onto the street was locked. The main entrance was a revolving door and it jammed when some of those escaping became stuck in it. An employee who tried to free the cable and open it was unsuccessful. With one door locked and another jammed, about two hundred people piled up in a terrified mass.

The fire traveled rapidly into the dining room and the New Cocktail Lounge on the Broadway side of the building. With the strangely moving flames came heavy black smoke and toxic gases that made many collapse in seconds, some before they could rise from their chairs. In this part of the building there was more trouble with exits. Several doors that would have provided escape to the street were locked; presumably so patrons could not escape without paying. Another door opened inward, and here again people trying to escape piled up.

The fire department was on hand almost immediately, for

someone had sent in a box alarm at 10:10 P.M. for an automobile fire on Broadway only a short distance from the nightclub. Firemen heard cries for help from Cocoanut Grove and turned at once to attend to this new situation, leaving two of their number to douse the smoldering seat cushion from the motor vehicle.

Then someone pulled a box on Piedmont Street on the other side of Cocoanut Grove at 10:21 P.M. The Deputy Chief, when he arrived, saw at once that this was a fire of the utmost seriousness. He went to the fire alarm box on Piedmont Street, "skipped" the second alarm, and sent in the signal for the third alarm. This saved time. He had set rolling the apparatus called for by two alarms; namely the second and the third. At 10:35 P.M. he sent in the fourth alarm and at 11:03 P.M. the fifth alarm and special calls for two more rescue companies. A total of twenty-three engine companies and five ladder companies, as well as a water tower and rescue companies, were at the scene.

The firemen did a good job in getting the fire out. It yielded fairly quickly to the hard-hitting streams of the great array of apparatus summoned by five alarms, and this in spite of the fact that a large proportion of the men were busy with the desperate work of rescue. The task of extinguishing the fire was easier because only the superficial material attached to the solid concrete structure was burning. Cloth and artificial palm trees, furniture, plywood, and scantling framework were soon drenched.

Yet even with the unusually speedy response provided by fire engines already nearby for the automobile fire, the damage was done. The terrible toll had been exacted before the cries for help came from the building to attract the attention of the firemen.

Black smoke ignited in the crowded foyer like an explosion, said witnesses. A massive ball of flame entered the main dining room, they said. Flames appeared in the air, without any fuel to feed on, as if gas were burning.

At the Broadway entrance a hundred were trapped when the panic-stricken crowd piled up against the door that opened inward. Overhead and all about the people trapped at the exits, strangely colored flames swirled and the lethal black smoke choked them. The firemen did their best to open the place up. Some windows that could have been good escape routes were filled in with glass bricks. These required hard work with axes and sledge hammers before they were opened.

When the dense black superheated smoke reached the open air, it ignited and blasted fire backward over the heads of those inside. Each time the firemen opened up part of the building, unburned gases would catch fire and flames would pour out.

In this ghastly nightmare 492 of the 1000 people in the place lost their lives, most of them then and there; some later in hospitals. Many were injured critically. The elements of this disaster stand forth with dreadful distinctness. Because they contain lessons that all should bear in mind, they are here enumerated:

1. The main revolving door jammed when one of those hurrying to escape through it was caught. The National Fire Protection Association Building Exits Code requires that when a revolving door is used, there shall be swinging doors next to it for emergency use. This place had no such swinging

doors. Moreover, a good exit door a few feet away was locked.

2. Other doors in this rambling building were locked so patrons could not leave without paying. This was a death warrant for many who might have escaped.

3. This concrete building, formerly a garage, was a first-class fire-resistive structure, as nearly fireproof as it could be until the designers "brightened up" the grim gray concrete. It is possible that the interior decorators who designed this lethal arrangement still thought of the building as fireproof. Were not the concrete walls and floor and ceiling still there?

For all who think they have fire safety because the building will not burn, we leave one simple thought. Nothing is more fireproof than an old-fashioned kitchen stove. But put a half bushel of pine edgings in there, light it, and nowhere will you find a hotter fire. That, in essence, is what had been done to the Cocoanut Grove building.

4. Gas was a large factor in the terrible death toll. We do not mean illuminating or heating gas or any commercial gas such as chlorine. We mean the hot gas given off by flammable materials that are heated until they decompose in an enclosed space where there is not enough oxygen to make combustion possible. These gases await the moment when there is enough oxygen. Then they burn, often rapidly enough to create an explosion or a flash fire. This happened in the Cocoanut Grove, so that flames appeared in the air. Some witnesses referred to a fire ball. Others said flame moved along the ceiling without actually proceeding from any material that was burning.

In some instances this gas was toxic or poisonous. Some patrons collapsed in their chairs. Some dropped to the floor as they headed for an exit, or what they hoped was an exit.

Some who got out collapsed on the sidewalk. In the hospitals many of the injured were found to be suffering from lung conditions.

This is in part explained by the fact that any gases of combustion are very dangerous and in fires less serious than this have accounted for deaths. Indeed, one of the standard precautions if one is in a building that is afire is to be careful about leaving a room and going into a hallway that may be charged with hot gas.

Yet in the Cocoanut Grove casualties such as this far exceeded what might be expected from the gases given off by an ordinary burning building. So puzzling were the unusual number of casualties that seemed to have been caused by some mysterious gas that expert studies were conducted to determine what occurred in those dreadful few minutes.

The careful and scholarly National Fire Protection Association examined the various theories advanced to account for the presence of this strange and lethal gas and the fact that few of the dead suffered serious external burns, but seem to have died of lung effects. The question certainly needed study by an organization of the stature of the National Fire Protection Association, which is recognized as second to none in this field. Explanations and theories to explain the disaster were being issued in quantity by people who were not capable of having an edifying opinion. These theories the National Fire Protection Association studied.

One theory was that so much liquor was consumed in the club that night that the atmosphere was charged with alcohol vapors from the breaths of patrons who had had a few and from liquor in glasses on the tables. These vapors, the theory was, ignited, and their presence throughout the place accounts for the rapid spread of the fire. This idea was seriously expounded by various writers in the public press, but the notion was useful only to give some newspaper men a sheet of interesting copy to hand to the editor.

Another theory was that the artificial leather on the walls, containing some pyroxylin, accounted for the lethal gases. Pyroxylin contains some cellulose nitrate, it burns very quickly and produces oxides of nitrogen, which are deadly gases. Consideration of this factor by the experts resulted in the conclusion that not enough pyroxylin was involved to have been a major element in the high death toll.

A third theory was that a quantity of motion-picture film might have been left somewhere about the premises in some concealed space or odd corner at an earlier time when the building was used as a film exchange. Nearby were several motion-picture film exchanges. Could an employee from one of them have dropped into Cocoanut Grove for a "quick one," perhaps meeting friends who persuaded him to have not one but several. If he had been carrying a few reels of film and had forgotten to take them all when he departed, they would have burned when the fire reached them and deadly gases would have resulted. Here again, as with the liquor fumes, we have mere speculation. No evidence of motion-picture film was ever discovered in the investigation.

Some suggested escaping gas from the refrigeration system. The report of the experts doubted that the copper tubing of the refrigeration system would have broken or melted in the early stages of the fire, which was when the deaths occurred.

There was a suggestion that various flameproofing chemicals were applied to the decorations in quantities too small to prevent the spread of the fire, yet in amounts that were enough to release poisonous gases when heated. Others suggested that an insecticide of a flammable nature had been used in the huge kitchen and these vapors helped spread the fire rapidly. The building had once been used as a garage as well as a film exchange. Could there, asked some, have been gasoline tanks under the basement floor that had never been completely drained. Here is more guesswork. No evidence of the presence of such chemicals was found during the investigation. After such a dreadful disaster it is not surprising that various far-fetched explanations should be advanced.

Two more suggestions were advanced in the wildly upset days following this ghastly tragedy. Some of the electric wiring had been installed by an unlicensed electrician who was suspected of overloading some circuits and not using proper fuses. Hot wires would cause the insulation on the wires to decompose, and give off toxic gases. However, the investigation revealed no wires that appeared to have burned off their insulation.

Finally, there was the thought that a fire had been smoldering in the concealed spaces between the cloth and artificial decorative material and the concrete wall. These spaces varied from a few inches to a few feet. Such a smoldering fire could have produced carbon monoxide and other deadly gases. But an examination of the ruins after the fire did not disclose evidence of any smoldering fire in any of the concealed spaces in the building.

The National Fire Protection Association's pamphlet on the fire describes all these theories, finding that no one of them furnishes a cause strong enough to account for any such destruction of life. Any fire, states the report, in such a highly combustible collection of materials and in an enclosed space where oxygen is soon exhausted, can create enough heat and carbon monoxide and smoke to cause widespread deaths and lung injuries.

Says the report, "the various other theories that have been advanced could furnish at best only a partial explanation." Of course, to get a sample of the smoke and fumes in those deadly first minutes of the fire was impossible. No one knows what was in that atmosphere. The report itself refers to "an element of mystery still unexplained." Note that even the National Fire Protection Association wondered if some strange and undiscovered element contributed to the disaster.

Can it be possible that this fire rapidly spreading in artificial palm trees and cotton-cloth decorations by its intense heat brewed a witch's cauldron of a composition like this:

1. Carbon monoxide, resulting from combustion in a place where there was insufficient oxygen.
2. Superheated air.
3. Poisonous gases resulting from the burning of ordinary building contents.
4. Oxides of nitrogen from burning pyroxylin.
5. Gases from some quantity of motion-picture film either in the room or in concealed wall spaces. Such gases are deadly.
6. Gases from flameproofing chemicals. Ammonia is one such gas.
7. Refrigerant gases.

If the fire released all or a large number of these factors by some peculiar combination of circmstances, then the result would have been this mysterious force that actually did strike down people by the hundreds. The experts analyze each one separately and dismiss it, but they fail to consider the possible combination of factors that might readily account for this symphony of death. And yet the study of most serious fires presents almost always a group, a combination, of unfavorable elements that, because they occur together, produce disaster of the first magnitude.

In our study of conflagrations we have seen that fires get out of hand at first because of an unfavorable combination of elements. This same principle very likely is the real basis of the Cocoanut Grove disaster.

The epilogue to the story of the fire is interesting and instructive.

From an outraged public arose a massive uproar only partly stilled by a long list of grand jury indictments. Ten defendants were obliged to stand trial in criminal court; manslaughter, conspiracy to violate the building laws, willful neglect of duty, neglect to enforce the fire laws, failure to report violations of the building laws and insufficient exits. Two were convicted. To report the names or even the positions of these defendants would not be right. They have suffered; those who were acquitted as well as those who were convicted.

Stricter laws and more rigid enforcement resulted. Revolving doors are now illegal in Massachusetts. Places of public assembly get a much closer scrutiny. Let us state here, as we have stated previously, that some of the burden of safety enforcement falls on the ordinary citizen. Officials cannot do it all.

Two couples at Cocoanut Grove that night were cautious folks. One of them discovered that the wall near him was hot. The two couples left the place, probably amid the jibes of the others in the group. But, when Cocoanut Grove burned in an epic holocaust, they were not characters in the drama of horror. They were elsewhere.

Probably the only bright part of this affair was the way in which some of the public organizations met the emergency. The fire department dealt with the fire promptly and efficiently. Helping them in the rescue work were many police officers, as is always the case in a serious fire. The U. S. Coast Guard put four hundred men into the fire fighting and rescue work, some of them arriving in trucks and beach wagons before the fifth alarm was in. Army and Navy personnel also worked hard in the rescue work. With over five hundred stretcher cases, the need for manpower was tremendous.

The Boston hospitals distinguished themselves. Not long after the third alarm the ambulances began screaming up to the doors of the accident wards. When the magnitude of the disaster was apparent, the hospitals put into effect plans already made to handle casualties in the event of an air raid. Doctors, nurses, and medical students, receiving the word by radio and telephone, came from as far away as thirty miles to report for duty. More than two hundred Navy medical corpsmen joined the effort at the scene of the fire.

The more serious burn cases had long stays in the hospitals. To them were devoted the services of the very best specialists and nurses and no effort or expense was spared. As a result, advances were made in the treatment of burns and in the medical techniques of skin grafting. New knowledge was acquired by doctors, particularly at Massachusetts General Hospital and Boston City Hospital, and the experience gained in this disaster was useful to the medical profession all over the country, particularly with the many victims of burns in military and naval engagements.

To describe all of the loss-of-life fires that have occurred in the United States and Canada would require a large volume. The ones here discussed are typical and it is hoped they are instructive, with lessons for all. We entertain the hope that readers have found herein lessons in this macabre field of knowledge that may enable them to encourage those who are constantly striving to make more safe the buildings in which large numbers of people assemble.

Some of us may be on a building committee, examining the architect's plans. We may be a member of a church where a fair or minstrel show is being held in the parish house. We may be on a school faculty or a member of a Parent-Teachers Association or a school committee. Or we may be a spectator or patron in some theater or at some exhibit. In any such instance what has been said in these pages is worth remembering.

In closing, here is the summary:

1. A fireproof building will not burn, but combustible contents will.

2. Are there enough exits? Are they clearly marked with signs? Have you looked around to see where they are?

3. Bear in mind that the state fire marshal or the fire-prevention bureau of the local fire department would like to be told of unsafe conditions anywhere.

4. Never refer to a person who talks of fire-protection mea-

sures and precautions as a crank or a fire nut or by any other disrespectful term. Sometimes he may be overzealous, but he is working for you.

5. If ever you have the opportunity to say a word in favor of installing sprinkler heads, say it. Think what a few sprinkler heads would have accomplished at Cocoanut Grove or in the Collinwood school or in that five-story lodging house. The sprinkler head is your friend, wherever you see it.

6. Are the exit doors locked? Find out. Will the windows open? Does someone think a window with glass bricks in it looks nice?

7. Remember that panic is a killer. In any emergency a level head is most valuable of all. Don't run or push. Reassure those around you. Yours might be the voice of leadership. One never knows.

8. And above all, when you see a dangerous condition, make a complaint, speak up. There are many kinds of courage. For most of them, there are no medals. The courage to speak up is one of the most valuable.

15

Chemical Fires

ONE OF THE outstanding characteristics of twentieth-century progress is the increasing use of chemicals in a vast number of industrial processes. Some of the giants of the business world are chemical companies. Few are the manufacturing operations that do not require chemicals. And a young man who specializes in chemistry in his college course is sure of a good job upon graduation.

The firemen, too, have been introduced to the Age of Chemistry, frequently the hard way. This is not to say that all chemicals are a fire hazard. Many are not; indeed some are excellent fire-extinguishing agents. Yet the list is long of chemicals that are on the flammable list. Many a chemical is in itself a good orderly citizen until the opportunity offers to combine with some other chemical for which it has an affinity. Some violent love affairs then result.

In most fires the presence of oxygen is a necessity. Not so with some chemicals. There is plenty of oxygen in their formulas. Engineers often say that a certain chemical compound decomposes. They mean that certain atoms leave the formula of that substance and unite with other departing atoms in the formula or in some nearby substance.

This decomposing process is a chemical reaction and many chemical reactions result in heat and expansion. There follows a fire or an explosion; frequently both. Many chemicals are "touchy," likely to behave violently with even the slightest encouragement or stimulus, and sometimes without any whatsoever. So, firemen will tell you, a chief characteristic of chemical fires is a big bang.

Engineers are engaged in a ceaseless search to make chemical processes and handling safe. A chemical plant is often located at a distance from other buildings; perhaps in an area of brushland or marsh. This is to prevent the spread of fire to other structures and to minimize injuries if an explosion does take place. The various groups of apparatus are built so the turn of a valve or the throwing of a lever cuts off the stream of chemicals passing into and out of each unit. Then, if fire develops, the flow of more material into the burning still or vat or tank or mixer is checked, thus reducing the fierceness of the fire and possibly allowing it to burn out.

A chemical plant has automatic installations for spraying whatever fire-extinguishing agent is proper on burning chemicals. They have a plant fire department trained in the use of spray, fog nozzles, foam generators, and streams, and in the use of extinguishing agents, such as sodium bicarbonate dust.

Personnel of a chemical plant are trained in disaster control. In some plants each group of employees has its own color of hat so that when a bad explosion occurs, a quick head count will tell the staff of disaster control how many men they have and how many are missing. Liaison with fire and police departments, civilian defense, the Red Cross, and hospitals is arranged in advance. Some companies have a plan for press conferences so that newspapers, television, and radio will not exaggerate the gravity of any occurrence.

It would be impossible for us to try to describe every chemical fire that has occurred in North America since the turn of the century, just as it would be too much to give an account of each major fire in tenements, hotels, or industrial occupancies. Therefore, what follows are examples to give some idea of this type of fire.

One of the most convenient of modern compounds is celluloid, because it can be molded into any form desired. It is also one of the touchiest of chemical combinations; upon contact with the tiniest flame it produces a ferocious flash fire. Householders have long since learned the danger of articles made of this material and are careful not to permit children to have celluloid toys.

Celluloid is used in the manufacture of women's shoes. In one shoe city the fire-prevention bureau was understandably nervous about the amount of celluloid scrap kicking around the floors of the local factories, so they persuaded the managements to have the scrap swept up frequently. Knowing full well that nothing in the way of fire safety would be gained if the scrap were kept in barrels or boxes in the basements or against the back walls of the various buildings, the fire-prevention bureau told the factories that if they would bring the celluloid scrap to the central fire station, one of the firemen would see to its disposal.

This plan worked well. In back of the fire station was a large vacant space where a fireman saw to burning this dangerous refuse at the very rear of the premises. One day a boy sent from a shoe factory appeared with a large gunny sack of celluloid scrap slung over his shoulder.

Down to the back of the lot went a fireman with this boy. Arriving at the spot the boy produced a cigarette and a wooden match. By way of demonstrating his maturity, he was about to scratch the match on the seat of his pants with the gunny sack of celluloid scrap still over his shoulder. The horrified fireman seized him by the wrist and snatched the match from his hand.

"Dump the stuff in that bag on the ground," ordered the fireman.

The boy did so and the fireman returned the match to him.

"Now back up two paces, scratch the match on the seat of your pants, which, by the way, is about where the bottom of that bag was hanging, and toss the match into that stuff."

The fireman had a hand on the boy's collar as the burning match arched into the celluloid. There was a tremendous *whoosh* as the scraps disappeared in one blast of flame. The fireman pulled the boy back another two steps as the stuff went off.

"See?" said the fireman. "Did you learn anything today?"

The young fellow, his face an ashen white, walked away, muttering.

In this same city was a concern called the Box Toe Company, specializing in the manufacture of celluloid shapes which it sold to the shoe factories. The building was a one-story concrete structure that by any standards would be adjudged fire proof. Inside, the manufacturing operation required the pouring of liquid celluloid into forms to make the box toes.

It is well known that most materials in a liquid state can and do vaporize. The fire-prevention inspectors were worried and puzzled as to what steps to take. No manufacturing city is ever free from the worry that some company may move to another community, taking with it the payroll and all the expenditures that help keep local business going. So the fire inspectors gave lectures to the management and kept their fingers crossed.

However, crossed fingers are no answer to the inexorable results of certain chemical combinations. One morning the work force arrived at the plant, the foreman unlocked the door, walked to the electric switch, and pulled down the lever to turn on the lights. He did not realize that in this tightly closed building was an accumulation of vaporized celluloid elements in exactly the right proportion to the oxygen of the atmosphere. It was the foreman's last act.

The mixture blew with a rushing, surging, swirling flame that blasted through the door, taking not only the foreman, but a dozen or so of the workmen. It surged from the windows and into a nearby dwelling, snuffing out the lives of six members of a family sitting at breakfast. Only one of the family survived; a boy who had gone to the bathroom on the other side of the house.

Above the building rose a vertical column of smoke and flame and at the top that phenomenon known as a fireball; a spherical body of smoke and gas and swirling, rolling flame.

A fireball results when a body of flammable gas is released from a confined space in which there is fire.

The noise of the explosion could be heard in the nearest fire stations. The firemen were dressed and on the apparatus, with the motors running and the house doors open, when the box hit. This was a morning when the second, the third, and the general alarms were sounded one minute apart.

Upon arrival, the firemen found half a dozen nearby wooden buildings burning briskly, and the concrete building was a roaring furnace. There were bodies to recover when it was possible to concentrate heavy streams so that men could get to them. There were injured people to lead to the waiting ambulances. Because there were not enough ambulances, trucks from nearby stores were pressed into service and the hospital staff had the sight of a line of laundry and grocery trucks at the emergency entrance. They had no time to remark on that odd circumstance; they were too busy.

The public uproar commenced at once, even before the twenty funerals of the victims. It was the fire-prevention bureau that suffered. A hearing took place at which considerable of the science of chemistry was paraded. The inspector who had covered the Box Toe Company had a hard time of it on the witness stand. During his ordeal he wished he had somehow acquired a degree in chemical engineering. He wished he had been tough with the owners of the factory, instead of thinking about the inconvenience and expense he might cause them if he insisted on changes

Out of it all came worthwhile results; lessons emphasized by this ghastly episode. First, it became even more clear that any operation involving powerful chemicals should be so located that there is sufficient open space around the plant.

The family in the nearby dwelling, engulfed by fire in this dreadful blast, were silent proof that such a precaution is imperative.

Second, any fire-prevention bureau must be given expert assistance when a problem of chemistry is presented by an occupancy such as this. It does not make sense to expect any fireman to answer a problem which requires a chemical engineer of consultant status.

Third, ventilation at all times is a necessity in any operation where flammable vapors occur. Properly designed windows or vents open twenty-four hours a day, or one or more power fans, would have prevented this factory from becoming charged with the flammable vapor that turned it into a giant incendiary bomb ready at a spark to produce a massive flash fire.

In many ways similar to the incident at the Box Toe Company was the Atlantic Pyroxylin Waste Company fire in North Arlingon, New Jersey, on June 9, 1933. This was a concrete block structure, eighty by fifty feet, in which a working force of twelve girls sorted pyroxylin scrap collected from factories in a wide industrual area.

The day had been very hot, with the thermometer reaching one hundred degrees. Across the road lay a small storehouse full of pyroxylin, and beyond that a beach at the river bank was thronged with bathers seeking relief from the oppressive heat.

Pyroxylin scrap swept up from a factory floor with machine oil on some of the material could constitute a situation where the substance might decompose. That word means chemical change and chemical change generates heat. That would set the stage for what is known as spontaneous ignition; meaning that the material catches fire by itself without the introduction of a flame or spark or a glowing substance such as a burning cigarette. Spontaneous ignition could have occurred here.

Another theory, which interested the police, was that a competitor of the company conceived the idea that burning material tossed into this building would produce a situation vastly simplifying their business picture. If this they thought, they were undeniably right. However, no evidence was ever uncovered to make this more than mere suspicion.

Whatever the fire's origin, certain facts are dismally clear. At 9:12 P.M. fire was seen coming through the roof. Shortly, there was more of a *puff* than an explosion, both ends of the building blew out, and a vast wave of flame rolled out over the nearby area. It killed five of a family in a nearby wooden dwelling, and snuffed out the lives of two women sitting on the front piazza of another nearby house on this hot evening.

The flames set fire to the small storehouse on the other side of the road. The pyroxylin inside burned furiously and another puff occurred. These sweeping flames killed a bather on the beach. The crowd on the beach took to the water and two were drowned. Eighty-three were so seriously burned they required hospital treatment.

The area was a bedlam of sirens of arriving fire apparatus and the panic-stricken screams of the bathers on the river beach. More sirens wailed as ambulances from every town in that part of the county, summoned by emergency calls, came to get the victims and rush them to hospitals.

At last the situation settled down to a simple fire-fighting problem. The firemen extinguished the wooden dwellings ignited by the rolling wall of flame, and they soaked with deluge sets the two buildings housing the pyroxylin operation, which by then were but hollow shells.

In this fire there were lessons; the same lessons as were taught by the Box Toe Company fire. As always, it is easier to see the text of the lesson than it is to learn it.

A classic example of a chemical fire occurred in New York City in the early part of this century in the days before we had the enormous development of industrial chemistry with quantities of sensitive materials measured not by ounces and pounds but by tons. The Tarrant Building was a drug warehouse in which was stored every kind of pharmacist's ingredient known to medical science.

One night fire involved a considerable area of this warehouse in which the shelves, boxes, bottles, packages, and barrels were loaded with material destined for druggist's prescriptions all over the country. Some of the chemicals burned, some baked and stewed in the heat and vaporized. Bottles broke, liquids ran out, fumes mixed with other fumes, acids ran over powders to produce reactions never planned. It was as if the devil himself had gone on holiday in a chemical laboratory, making mixtures that to any good chemist would be a series of nightmares.

Into this building went the firemen to extinguish the fire. And out they came, some walking, some staggering, some being carried. This, they finally concluded, must be fought from the outside, and from positions to windward. They got the fire out before it spread to any other building, and no chemistry expert ever tried to guess what strange combinations of nature's elements were in the smoke that night. The firemen were sure that all the noxious compounds known to science could have been found in there by any chemist competent to make a test.

In the Tarrant fire there was no considerable quantity of any one chemical. Therefore, the explosions that took place were not heavy ones.

On August 25, 1965, a fire involving large quantities of chemicals occurred in the Dupont Works at Louisville, Kentucky. The situation became serious immediately. The plant was located in an industrial district of two square miles called Rubbertown. Eight hundred and fifty were at work there at the time of the fire.

One of the operations in this plant was a process for converting acetylene into monovinyl acetylene, termed MVA. Upon the completion of the process the MVA gas was piped into nearby storage tanks under pressure. To do this a compressor was necessary. Some of the moving parts of the compressor failed and overheated, causing MVA gas being circulated to decompose. This means an explosion when such materials are involved.

The first explosion, a major one, occurred at 9:28 A.M. Then, within the next thirteen minutes, ten more explosions ripped through the MVA apparatus, killing twelve men and injuring sixty.

The plant had a plan for such an emergency. From the control center issued the order to put the plan into effect. These are the steps.

1. Operators of various units in the many chemical processes in the plant began shutting down their equipment and taking measures to isolate their units.

2. Word went out for the evacuation of the plant.

3. The evacuation of people in residences within a radius of danger was ordered.

4. Evacuation of personnel from nearby plants in Rubbertown began.

5. All traffic on the Ohio River, upon the bank of which the Dupont plant stood, was halted. Traffic on the state highway on the opposite bank of the river was stopped.

6. Nearby airfields were notified to detour all air traffic so no aircraft would pass above the plant area.

7. Fire apparatus, police, ambulances, and Civilian Defense units over a wide mutual-assistance area received the alarm and headed for the scene.

8. All personnel withdrew to a distance of a half mile. The Dupont plant Disaster Control Group set up headquarters at a distance of half a mile.

9. A head count was made of all plant personnel. This was made easy because all employees wore hard hats, a military-type helmet that protects the skull from falling objects. The helmets were of a different color for each department, which made a quick count easier. In this case, the head count revealed that some men working on the MVA process were missing.

The foregoing indicates a large degree of forethought, organization, and planning. This was due to a realization throughout the chemical industry of the hazards and potentialities of disaster in this type of manufacturing. The dangers had received dreadful emphasis at Texas City on April 16, 1947, when a fire occurred in the hold of the ship *Grandcamp,* loading ammonium nitrate. The ship exploded and four hundred were killed, including the firemen who were aboard.

When the ship exploded, the nearby Monsanto Chemical plant caught fire and burned fiercely. Two other ships caught fire, one of which had sulphur and nitrates aboard. Both ships blew up. Eight oil tanks ashore burned. Warehouses built of reinforced concrete were destroyed along with many other structures. The fire burned two days, a thousand were killed, four thousand injured, the loss was $67,000,000. The destruction extended far beyond the ships and the Monsanto plant.

The Dupont fire was not nearly as much of a disaster. The loss was $10,000,000, the casualties moderate. That this was not as much of a disaster was due in some part to the carefully prepared plan, but more due to the fact that the materials involved were not present in such tremendous quantities as the 1400 tons of ammonium nitrate and the other materials at Texas City. The plan was developed to protect lives against maximum hazard and it is maximum hazard that must be considered whenever any chemical plant has a major fire.

The Dupont fire was bad enough, yet the fire-fighting forces managed to get it out. Ruptured water mains were hurriedly put back in service, sprays were rigged to protect nearby tanks, existing fires were extinguished. The plant firemen had been well trained. Plant fire-fighting facilities were carefully planned. This was a bad fire, yet it could have been much worse.

The authorities found from this experience that two improvements were desirable. One was to provide for efficient communications for disaster-control headquarters. The other concerned relations with news media. A system of press conferences with newspaper, radio, and television reporters seems necessary so that exact facts may be reported.

At the Dupont fire, when the alarms went out over a wide area, the roads resounded to the screaming sirens of fire apparatus, ambulances, police cars, and civilian-defense trucks. The alarm came over tappers and radios in two dozen fire stations. Newspapers, of course, have tappers and radios. Everyone who knows reporters knows that they lose not a minute in getting to the scene of any story. And we know, further, that the story gets full value in the telling. The first reports are likely to give an impression of dire disaster. The excitement of leaping flame, rolling clouds of smoke, and fire apparatus racing in from distant points create a psychology we all know, having experienced it.

So an important feature of a disaster-control plan is a series of conferences to give facts to the news media so that they will not make the situation any worse than it actually is.

Some of the worst chemical fires have involved ships. The reason is a simple one; large quantities. A ship has always been the most economical way to move a large quantity of anything. Therefore, when a temperamental chemical acts up on a ship, it is not a problem of a truckload or a carload. The quantity may be over a thousand tons, as in the Texas City disaster.

Furthermore, spaces aboard ship are confined and hard to reach with a stream of water. They are exactly the sort of place where gas pressure can build up conditions favorable to an explosion. Often the fire-fighting equipment aboard ship is not at all equal to a fire involving large quantities of volatile materials, so hose lines have to be dragged aboard from ashore. Firemen have a difficult time of it when they try to get lines aboard ship and it is even more difficult to find a position from which to direct a stream at the seat of the fire.

One ship fire we attended personally; the Danish ship *Laila* moored at a pier in Charlestown, which is part of Boston. On March 10, 1937, we were headed for Boston on a railroad known locally as the Narrow Gauge, the full name being Boston, Revere Beach & Lynn Railroad. Riding through Revere we saw to the west of us an enormous cloud of whitish smoke ascending straight upward, for there was little wind.

The Narrow Gauge delivered its passengers at its wharf in East Boston, where they went aboard one of the ferry boats owned by the railroad and were transported to Rowe's Wharf on Atlantic Avenue, Boston. The enormous smoke column was even more plainly visible as the sidewheel ferry took us across Boston Harbor.

This, we decided, required a taxi, so with a driver who became more interested with every block we traveled, we headed for the column of smoke. Arriving in the area, we went down a ramp in the taxi into the dock area, managed to persuade a police officer that our presence there was tremendously important, and with the meter ticking we swept up to the fire scene like the commissioner himself.

The *Laila* carried a cargo of sodium nitrate. The fire had taken possession of the holds, and was almost impossible to get at. A fire burrowing along in merchandise of any kind stowed below decks is the most frustrating situation a fire department ever faces. It is impossible to hit it with a stream, no matter how many good streams are available.

Twenty-seven engine companies and three fireboats were

slugging away with everything they had, yet the vast clouds of white smoke continued to roll up from all parts of the *Laila.* The many streams directed down into the hatches were not hitting the seat of the fire.

We were standing well back, near a string of box cars on one of the spur tracks, when the explosion let go. It spouted from a hatch like a volcano. Broken boards and timbers and all manner of debris shot upward. The men shut down their lines and fled across the deck to get clear of the blast. This explosion was not a big bang, but rather a rushing, pushing wave of pressure. We can recall vividly the slight squeaking noise of the springs in the undercarriage of the boxcar behind us as it rocked sideways when the pressure wave reached it.

There was no blast of flame. The explosion was from confined gases in the hold below, and the entire cargo was not involved. It would be classed as a minor explosion, as we shall see presently.

The firemen returned immediately to their problem with streams that, it is estimated, were delivering 35,000 gallons a minute into the burning cargo. The water, although not hitting directly at the seat of the fire, soaked the cargo and flooded the lower part of the hold. At last they got it out.

In the freight yard near the pier we met Alton Hall Blackington, beloved friend of everyone who ever was present at a major fire in the area. As always, he had his camera with him, so that he might add a few pictures for the lectures he gave so well. Blackie, as everyone called him, seemed worried, and we soon found out why. The fire was subdued now, but he told us that all he could think of while it was really going was the Halifax disaster twenty years earlier, in 1917. This fire, he said, had the same circumstances, and if the end of the fire had been the same, over two dozen Boston fire companies, a good crowd of spectators, and Blackie and his famous camera would all have been posted missing. As to this, Blackie was quite correct. We agreed with him that this day Boston had got off easy.

Two other episodes involving chemical cargoes and ships ended differently, and any one reading these pages will be happy that he was not present. The first of these is the story of the ship *Fort Stikene* in the harbor of Bombay, one of the great cities of India. On April 13, 1944, this vessel arrived in port with over 1300 tons of high explosives aboard, including TNT, and a large cargo of cotton. The next day, April 14, fire was discovered in a lower hold in the bales of cotton. The ship's hose lines were operated, but with no effect. The Bombay Fire Department arrived with a first-alarm response and went to work on what appeared to be a small fire in the hold.

Although more fire apparatus was summoned, the seat of the fire was not located. Streams were turned on the cases of TNT to keep them below ignition temperature, while the firemen and engineering experts from ashore worked desperately to locate and extinguish the fire.

The fire-fighters were not "getting" this fire. Heat in the burning hold became intense, smoke and steam blanketed the ship. After a four-hour battle, the order was given for all aboard to abandon ship. Before all the men were ashore the TNT exploded and forty firemen were killed.

Structures on the wharves were leveled, and big waves activated by the blast moved across the harbor. Other ships caught fire. A second and greater explosion followed, blowing the *Fort Stikene* and a nearby ship into fragments. A wave of flame started many other fires. The explosion and resulting fires destroyed nineteen ships and a hundred acres of the city. Nine hundred people were killed and two thousand injured. This one was an $80,000,000 loss.

At Halifax, Nova Scotia, on December 6, 1917, occurred the worst of all of the episodes involving those very sensitive combinations of chemicals termed explosives. It was war time and convoys were assembled in the magnificent harbor of Halifax with its famed Bedford Basin and Northwest Arm.

From Halifax the convoys and their escorting warships would sail for England, proceeding through waters in which the deadly German submarines prowled, ready to send torpedoes at any cargo ship. Into Halifax harbor came the French ship *Mont Blanc* to join a convoy. She was loaded with war materials, including an amount of TNT which some accounts estimate as high as four thousand tons. As a deck load she carried thirty-five tons of benzol in steel drums.

About 9:00 A.M. in the ship channel the Belgian freighter *Imo,* by some mismanagement on the bridge, collided with the *Mont Blanc.* The two ships drew apart without much damage. However, some of the benzol drums were ruptured by the blow the *Imo* struck and this liquid, a first cousin to gasoline, ran out and drizzled down below the deck. Somehow it came in contact with a spark or flame and a fire broke out. Flames and black smoke rose from the deck where the benzol drums were lashed in place.

The captain of the French ship and his crew, aware of the nature of their cargo, reacted with great promptness, not by a vigorous attack upon the fire, but by lowering the life boats and pulling for the shore. They were last seen entering the woods on the Dartmouth side of the harbor. Without a crew, the *Mont Blanc,* with a brisk fire burning, drifted toward the Halifax harbor front and shortly struck one of the Richmond piers.

An alarm sent in from a street box brought some apparatus of the Halifax Fire Department. At the same time a boat from HMCS *Niobe* and a boat from HMS *Highflyer* headed for the *Mont Blanc.* Their men boarded the ship and attacked the fire. The behavior of the two boat crews, one from the Canadian Navy and one from Britain's Royal Navy, is worth noting here. They were magnificent. As always, the King's Navy needed only to be shown the enemy. Their reactions from then on are wholly predictable, no matter what the odds, as many an enemy over the centuries has discovered.

But here in Halifax harbor the odds were too great. The *Mont Blanc* exploded before the men had been aboard long; they vanished in a blast that has been called the greatest ever to take place on the face of patient old Mother Earth. This, of course, was before Hiroshima, yet the explosion probably has been but little exceeded by anything the Atomic Age has visited upon us.

The pillar of smoke, reported one observer, rose a mile high, "unfolding at the top like an incredible toadstool." The explosion rattled windows in Truro, sixty miles away. Far at sea the American warships *Tacoma* and *Von Steuben* heard the blast and steamed full speed for Halifax, arriving in time to land rescue parties of sailors, marines, and medical personnel.

The Richmond district of the waterfront, one mile square, was leveled. Fourteen hundred were killed outright and six hundred died later of injuries. The city's newest fire engine was wrecked on the way to answer the street box that had been pulled and its entire crew was killed. The chief of the department was killed while speeding to the fire in his motor car. Most of the dead were in the nearby waterfront section, but not all. A descending steel fragment killed a brakeman on a train two miles away. One of the *Mont Blanc's* fleeing crew a mile distant fell victim to another steel fragment.

In the harbor the captain and thirty of the crew of the Belgian ship *Imo,* which had started all this by ramming the *Mont Blanc,* were killed by the blast and fragments. On the British cruiser there were casualties, one being a sailor whose head was crushed when the force of the blast slammed him against a steel gun turret. Fragments fell all over the city. The force of the blast blew in countless windows, and flying glass cut faces and hands to shreds. The force of the shock wave tore ships from their moorings at the wharves and from their anchorages in the roadstead.

An observer later referred to "the great globe of fiery gas that wrecked buildings and the fire in this wave that ignited the splintered ruins of a square mile of buildings." The firemen, naval and military parties, and volunteers finally managed to extinguish the fires in the wreckage and debris. The destruction was ended, leaving to the people of Halifax the task of burying the dead, caring for the thousands of wounded, and patching up the shattered buildings that still stood. The ruined dwellings had to shelter the people against the bitter northern winter.

That night, as thousands worked at searching ruins for bodies, setting up temporary hospitals for the wounded, covering empty windows from which the glass had been blasted, and trying to restore heat in buildings whose chimneys had been blown down, a fierce blizzard hit the city. Somehow the people managed to get through this newest trial, huddling together for warmth in heatless and partially wrecked houses.

The other cities of North America quickly came to the aid of near prostrate Halifax. From Massachusetts came a relief ship with doctors, nurses, food, motor trucks and gasoline, clothing, medicine, and bedding. A railroad train set out from Boston, loaded with relief supplies. Massachusetts contributed half a million dollars and sent a Relief Commission to conduct clinics and do welfare work. From all sources $30,000,000 was contributed. Slowly the city recovered from this great explosion.

Any German military or naval force that had succeeded in causing such destruction to the enemy as at Halifax and at Bombay would most certainly have had the Iron Cross bestowed upon every man in it. Yet these blows were achieved by no military or naval force. They occurred at Halifax and at Bombay because dangerous chemicals were not handled carefully.

Lessons from these events are not hard to find. Explosives must be handled with great care. Large quantities should not be placed in one ship or building. A vessel handling such cargo must be berthed at points distant from other ships. Explosives should be divided into small lots before being shipped. In the hurry and hustle of war, many sound safety rules are overlooked. That is the true explanation at Halifax and at Bombay. It was war.

16

When Forests Burn

WE HAVE already noted that all serious fires result from a combination of unfavorable factors. This is even more true of forest fires than it is of fires in a settled community. With snow on the ground a bad fire can occur in a large building and may develop so that it involves many buildings if the situation is such that radiated heat can attack nearby wooden walls and break windows.

However, a forest fire is completely impossible with snow on the ground or while it is raining. Weather is the big factor in forest fires. In wet weather they cannot happen. In certain other weather situations those who must fight forest fires make sure that their equipment is ready and then they wait for the alarm they know is sure to come. From experience they recognize the combination of weather conditions most likely to produce a bad fire.

A long period without rainfall, low humidity, and a brisk wind are some of the major unfavorable factors. The final unfavorable factor is a set of circumstances favoring the start of fire. Were there nothing to ignite a forest, those charged with the duty of protecting our Western timberlands and the firemen in the towns of the East could indeed have an easy life of it, even when the weather is dry and windy.

The causes of forest fires vary in different localities. In our Western forests the circumstances favoring the start of fire are as follows:

1. The hunting, camping, and fishing seasons. Vacationists, many of them city folks, fail to understand the danger of leaving a camp fire burning, or the results that may follow if a cigarette is flipped into bushes or dry grass. When these people come rolling into the National Forests with their gear for some good, wholesome outdoor activity, the Forest Service men on duty in the fire towers scan the landscape very carefully for a telltale trace of smoke.

2. Lumbering operations can cause a fire if someone throws a cigarette aside carelessly or if the crew at the mill burn edgings, bark, or sawdust on a bad day without a close watch on their fire.

3. Incendiary. All the mentally ill are not immured in hospitals and asylums; there are a considerable number at large. Many people find a fire to be an interesting variation from the normal, as witness the large crowds present at any major fire and most minor ones. Were an interest in fires evidence of mental illness, the public treasury would be exhausted in building institutions to contain the vast number of persons suffering from that aberration. It is when an individual is without an understanding of right and wrong that

we have the problem of a deranged person who is unaware of the danger that lies in setting a fire and the criminality of it.

Incendiarism sometimes is committed by persons near the pauper level who hope to be employed on the crew the forest wardens will raise to battle the fire. The mental condition of such persons is questionable.

4. In the Western forests more fires are ignited by lightning than any other cause. U. S. Department of Agriculture's Forest Service Bulletin No. 130 states that 56 percent of the fires in Western areas are caused by lightning. The bulletin notes that there is a record of 1100 lightning-caused fires in one period of two weeks. In the West it is not uncommon to have thunderstorms without any rain, a phenomenon absolutely unheard of in the Eastern part of the United States.

And in the East forest fires started by lightning do not occur. Eastern lightning is of the same power. Let not anyone suppose that Westerners can boast of bigger and better lightning bolts. In the East the thunderstorm is accompanied by a downpour and nothing could ignite the woodlands sodden with rain. An Eastern lightning bolt often ignites the dry interior of an attic or the hay in a barn loft and sometimes strikes dead a person sheltering under a tall pine, fishing with a steel pole, or near a good conductor in a building. But Eastern woodlands are safe from lightning.

Fires start in the Eastern part of the country from some of the same causes. Hunters, campers, and fishermen from the city cause their share. So do lumbermen, so do incendiary criminals.

In the East there is another cause; the suburbanite. The towns within commuting range of big cities have grown rapidly because so many city people have moved out to the open spaces or have summer camps. These city fellows have no background of experience in living beyond the areas of concrete sidewalks. It is in the warm, pleasant weekends of early spring that these chaps are dangerous. The sky is blue, the sun is warm, the breeze is gentle, and they are yearning to be out of doors after a winter of restricted activity.

One of the notions a city fellow frequently has is that if the dry grass is burned off a field, the new grass will be encouraged and will appear very shortly. So it will, for in the spring it is growing beneath the protective shield of dry grass from last year. What he does not know is how fast a fire will travel in dry grass if the wind freshens even a little. Maybe he has a fire going to burn brush and papers and old stalks and leaves from last year's garden and this fire is near dry grass.

It usually happens when he goes into the house to get a cookie and a glass of ginger ale or walks over to talk crops with a neighbor. The fire has started to travel. He dashes out with a broom to put it out. The fire is across the grass, into a brush patch, and has involved a group of young pines.

At about this point our suburbanite yells to his wife to telephone the fire department. The bull whistle on the town hall blasts away. Soon there are sirens. The apparatus arrives with men and boys hanging all over it, followed by a dozen or so automobiles full of townspeople ready to turn to in the critical early moments of the fire. If they are lucky, they get it out with streams from the booster lines that take water from the big tank on each engine, plus a couple of dozen men with "packpumps," which are five-gallon tanks carried on a man's back with a little pump that throws an excellent small stream. More men go in with brooms and with shovels and perhaps a few soda and acid two-and-a-half-gallon "pony chemical" tanks.

A first-alarm response in a small town on an April weekend when there is a sizable group hanging around the fire station, and many others working around home and ready to respond, brings a remarkably powerful force early in the fire. They get most of these fires out quickly. Back to quarters they go. Recall is sounded—two blows on the whistle—and they are ready for the next one as soon as they fill their tanks and recharge their soda and acid pony chemicals. The chief may stay behind for a few moments to acquaint the suburbanite with a few of the facts of life in the country. Such conversations often contain a considerable quantity of hard language.

Recounted above is the optimum outcome. The result may be different if the town fire department is busy with a fire elsewhere or if there is even a few minutes' delay in sending in the alarm. Then the men may not be able to head off the fire with a quick attack with booster lines, pack pumps, brooms, shovels, and chemical tanks. If they do not succeed in getting in front of the fire, it may go off through brush and pines, entirely out of hand.

Then the department must hurry to get around to whatever road lies beyond, for by the time the fire gets there it may be hot enough to take whatever houses are on the road. At this point the chief, if he is wise, will see if he can get two or three pieces of apparatus from nearby towns to help him at the fire and another piece to "cover in" at his fire station.

Here luck plays its part in the combination of unfavorable factors we have mentioned. If it is a bright, warm, breezy April weekend, other towns in the area may be occupied with emergencies. And suppose that in the direction the fire has taken, there is no road the department can use to get in front of the fire. There might be two miles of woodland before a pond or river or road or another town can offer any obstacle to the onward march of the fire. Should this be the situation, the firemen settle down to fight a bad one. No quick blows can settle it. Such a fire requires a long, laborious, tedious, and expensive campaign.

The pumping engines take positions at hydrants, a brook, or a pond as near to the fire as possible. Each runs a two-and-a-half-inch line in as far as its hose supply will allow, and at the end they connect a Y from which two smaller lines run farther into the fire area. Probably they can thus reach a part of the fire. From the forest-fire wagon which most town departments have the portable pump is lifted and manhandled into the woods. The small hose is dragged along by other men.

Town firemen know where every brook, pond, or water hole is. They will horse the portable pump into the woods until they reach such a location, set it down, and drop their suction hose into the water. While they try to get the pump going by a suitable admixture of language and mechanical skill, other men are dragging the hose to the edge of the fire. This type of hose varies from one to one and a half inches in diameter and gives a stream that will knock down any fire except one in an evergreen thicket.

The stream from the portable will take care of an important length of the perimeter of the fire, with a good crew of men to drag the hose from one position to another. The men with the streams taken from the Y on the end of each line from the regular pumping engines can take care of another large length of the fire's perimeter.

But a forest fire that has gotten away has a very large perimeter. The men with the pack pumps, returning to a water source for refills, work away on the fire line. So do the men with the shovels and the brooms, although in a brisk brush fire a broom handle is not long enough and the man using it often finds his face is getting scorched by the heat.

When a fire gets away, the chief sends back to town for more men and boys. The boys know exactly what to do when they arrive, for they are experienced. One of them uses a hatchet to cut through the roots and sod of the forest floor until he has an area of loose dirt about four feet wide. The other boys, with pails, fill them with loose dirt and get up to the fire line where they can throw the moist earth at the base of the flames, thus knocking the fire down. What fire is left can be taken care of by a man with a broom, who sweeps burning material inward onto the already burned surface.

These dirt crews and the hose-line crews are all working on the sides of the fire, keeping it from spreading sideways, narrowing it down. The chief by this time has put in a call for help to a state or county forest-fire crew, They may be engaged elsewhere, but if he is lucky he will get one.

The state truck may carry another portable pump with a big supply of hose that will take a water source and get another good stream onto the fire. Or it may be a "brush breaker," a big four-wheel-drive truck with a steel shield over the front and a water tank of possibly a thousand gallons capacity. This machine can go through any area of brush and small trees, pushing the growth aside or rolling over it.

Here is the strength to get in front of the fire. The brush breaker can move across the fire front with the man riding on the tank directing a strong stream of water into the base of the fire. He knocks it down and the men with the hand tools can deal with what remains of it, for the stream will have taken the heat out of it.

With help from other towns, even though they are towns at a distance, with the help of state and county crews and all the manpower of the town that can be recruited, they generally narrow down the fire and get it out. Sometimes it burns along until it runs into another town, there to be met at some roadway by another fire department and possibly one or more additional state or county units. Or the end may come at a natural firebreak such as a pond or river.

A major emergency like this on a day when the weather makes forest fires general in the area may cause an extremely critical situation if an alarm is sounded for a fire elsewhere in town. On one such day a fire in a wide expanse of woodland in Reading and North Reading, Massachusetts, required the attention of all available apparatus and men in several surrounding towns. The situation was so bad that an old Amoskeag steam fire engine used by the Wakefield Water Department for pumping out flooded areas was pressed into service to draft from a pond in the fire area.

At the height of this battle a fire broke out in a dwelling house in the residential part of Reading. Every piece of kit in every nearby town was at work on the big forest fire or at a half-dozen smaller but dangerous ones. The Reading fire alarm operator, wishing there were two of him, scrambled to find a fire engine. Frantic telephoning located one in Everett, a wholly urban community ten miles away and near Boston. A fully manned pump left the Everett station and with siren wide open went screaming through Malden, Melrose, and Wakefield. None of these towns had a piece in service. From Wakefield the pump rolled into Reading, where a police officer on a motorcycle met them and led them to the fire.

The blaze in the dwelling house had progressed while this hurried search for fire apparatus was going on. However, it was a fire that one good engine line could dispose of and the firemen from four towns away drenched it and saved most of the building.

One frequent cause of forest fires, the steam locomotive, is no longer a hazard. Although some of the romance of the railroad disappeared when the diesel locomotive took over the work of hauling the nation's trains, a cause of fires was removed.

A steam locomotive keeps its fire hot by exhausting steam from the cylinders into the smoke box. This creates a strong draft. This draft pulls red-hot coals from the firebox and they sprout out of the smokestack when the locomotive is working steam. The exhaust from the cylinders is strongest when the train is being started. In some country railroad stations there was a point a few hundred yards up the track where a brisk brush fire could be counted on once a year. Spark-arrester screens were installed in the smokestacks on some lines. These, however, interferred with the draft, and if the engine was not steaming well, one of the crew climbed up and knocked a few holes in the screen. This improved the draft, but the sparks were no longer arrested.

In the West and in a few sections of the East where lie great tracts of forest with few settlements or none at all, the technique of fire-fighting must be different. In such places there is no bull whistle and motor fire engines roaring down paved roads with a gang of townspeople hanging onto the apparatus, no hydrants, no calls for out-of-town help.

The federal government is responsible for vast national forests. In some Western states privately owned timberlands constitute a large proportion of the area not occupied by the national parks and forests. Federal, state, and local fire-fighters are organized to deal with vast areas and to act with great speed.

As in all fires, the critical time is when a fire first starts. Fire-watch towers cover every important forest area. If the tower man sees any sign of smoke, he ascertains its location by consulting a grid map and telephones the message to headquarters, where a "dispatcher" is in charge. The nearest ground unit is sent to the fire in its truck.

In the U. S. Forest Service are 350 men trained as smoke jumpers. The nearest of these units boards an airplane and heads for the fire, which may be in some difficult and roadless mountain area which the truck crew cannot reach until they have dismounted and trudged up a steep trail.

Over the fire scene the smoke jumpers leave the airplane and parachute down. They often land on difficult terrain, but the parachute has steering slots and the man tries to guide his descent so that he may come to earth in a favorable spot. Each man has a rope, so that if he lands in a tree, he may let himself down.

By another parachute his tools, rations, water canteen, and first-aid kit descend. As soon as he has retrieved them, he is ready to go to work on the fire. If he is far from a road, it will be some time before the truck crew arrive to assist. But the smoke jumpers start digging a fire line to check the oncoming flames. On the records are hundreds of instances where they have controlled the fire before the arrival of the ground forces.

In the West great emphasis is laid on making a fire line ahead of the fire and finally running the line entirely around the burning area. A fire line is mostly a digging job, with some cutting if there is brush or young trees where the line is to be constructed. When a safe line is built with a good width of dirt, the crew then proceeds to backfire, a technique rarely used in the East. The backfire is set on the side of the line, or dirt area, which is toward the oncoming flames. When the backfire and the main fire meet, all the fuel within the line that has been constructed is consumed and the fire goes out.

There is a mopping-up operation, when the men deal with stumps, log piles, and dead trees that are still burning. The operation we have sketched here is a small fire, with an ideal outcome. Many times the fire is entirely beyond the capabilities of the smoke jumpers and the first truckload of ground crew. A bad one may have a perimeter of miles and call forth all the resources of federal, state, local, and private fire-fighters.

In a serious fire, men are mobilized from over great distances. Large crews are formed and taken to the fire scene. A camp is organized, sometimes several, and a commissary to feed crews numbering into the hundreds. The leaders direct these gangs of men in digging the lines to contain the fire. Bulldozers and tractor-drawn plows are brought into the battle to extend the fire line and broaden it.

Into the fight are brought aircraft, air tankers carrying up to 6000 gallons. There are various liquids used for extinguishing agents; sodium calcium chloride, bentonite clay, borate, calcium chloride are some of the chemicals used with water to form a slurry to drop on the ground to act as a fire retardant. These compounds are wet and they form a film over fuels on the ground to check the spread of the flames. Sometimes the planes, and helicopters as well, are used to get in the first blow, with the purpose of slowing and reducing the fire so that when the ground crews arrive, they will have a better chance of controlling the blaze. Sometimes the airplanes drop the various slurries on a large fire out of control to add their bit to the other measures being taken.

A big Western fire can have a perimeter of fifty to a hundred miles and involve twenty to fifty thousand acres. The Forest Service states that in 1960 they had 25,000 men fighting fire at one time and nearly as many in 1961 at ten major fires in the Western states. In fires of that magnitude, every resource is thrown into the fight, including aircraft. Two hundred airplanes are now available to drop the various slurries, and fifteen helicopters and twenty tanker planes may be working on one of the big fires.

It is in the big ones that the most feared thing occurs; the crown fire. This is a fire that travels in the tops of evergreen trees. It roars through the resinous tops of the pines, or other evergreens. It goes above the heads of the firefighters and comes to the ground again to the rear of the men.

A crown fire may easily trap men between two areas of fire, and the lives of some of the gallant men of the Forest Service have thus been lost.

Another peculiarity of a fire in the woods is the behavior of a burning root. It can smolder for days, and then the fire will reappear at the surface several feet away. This is particularly dangerous if the burning root passes under the trench that has been dug for a fire line. It can result in a rekindling in the dry grass, pine needles, and forest duff on the other side of the line.

It is well recognized by intelligent people that forest fires represent an important national loss. To begin with, nothing more dismally scars the face of nature than a tract of burned woodland. Fire leaves a dead area of gaunt, lifeless tree trunks and worthless scrub growth on the ground.

The loss of timber is appalling. It is now realized that our forest resources are not limitless. So a large fire in the Western lumber states, in Maine, the Adirondacks, Michigan, or Wisconsin is a disastrous waste of natural wealth. Such a fire ruins fishing streams, destroys wild life, and robs ravines and valleys of the trees, bushes, moss, and grass that check excessive runoff of rain. A heavy rain drips slowly down through the branches of trees, and the root systems and duff of the forest floor pick up the water. It is estimated that one large tree absorbs a barrel of water.

A valley denuded by fire one year is likely to produce a destructive flood the next year. A good tract of woodland is one of the best flood-control elements there is. Without it the water cascades unchecked down from the hills, tearing gullies in the slopes. Mud and sand are carried down and more sediment is added as the racing waters swiftly pass over the rich fields of valley farms.

Apart from loss of land by erosion, loss of timber that could be cut and taken to sawmills for lumber, and destruction of scenes of great natural beauty, there is a further evil to be kept in mind at all times. Under the most unfavorable circumstances, a forest fire can develop such heat, fury, and volume that whole communities are blotted out.

This happened in Wisconsin in 1872 on the day of the Chicago fire. After a long drought a fire driven by high winds raced through bone-dry woodlands to overwhelm the town of Peshtigo and several other little towns in the woods. Nothing remained. Many were killed by a wall of fire so intense that even some of those who submerged themselves in the river did not survive.

The same thing happened in October 1918 in the forests of Minnesota. In Maine in 1947, with adverse weather conditions, fire swept down on Mount Desert, part of the famed Bar Harbor summer resort, and when it was finally over, 172 houses lay in ruins. In Oregon in 1932 and 1933 fires destroyed choice standing timber that amounted to a year's lumber supply.

California has suffered heavily from forest fires that have swept into large communities with an intensity that has been too much for strong, well-organized fire departments. Berkeley suffered severely on September 17, 1923, when a brush fire attacked the city, destroying 640 buildings. The villain of the piece was, as in many other sweeping fires, the wooden shingle roofs.

This Berkeley disaster was further proof of the terrible menace of wooden shingle roofs whenever a fire happens to get out of hand on a dry, windy day. The lesson had already been learned by most communities from such costly demonstrations as Salem and Chelsea. In 1930 the Nashua conflagration presented another instance.

In Los Angeles these various conflagrations appear to have escaped the notice of the authorities. Wooden shingle roofs were still legal in Los Angeles on November 5, 1961. This was a day of low humidity and a brisk wind. A dry spell had long continued.

These weather conditions are elements favorable to the occurrence of a bad fire. So were the wooden shingle roofs. That was not all. The Brentwood and Bel Air districts were areas of expensive homes, a high-value district of premium residences. Well-to-do people had lavished money and care on constructing interesting and picturesque dwellings on the hills and in the ravines of this foothill country.

Winding and deadend roads were common. Houses built on the slopes of the ravines were numerous, and the downhill sides of these houses were supported on stilts. On the ground beneath these houses frequently grew the chaparral bushes, lending to the residence a more romantic and country appearance. The out-in-the-country appearance was further enhanced by chaparral brush growing as close as ten feet to some of the houses.

Add another factor. The chaparral bush is of high oil content and is said to be the most combustible bush in North America. And the Santa Ana or "devil wind," a very dry northeast wind, was blowing that day.

The Los Angeles Fire Department was aware that this was a bad day for a fire. At 8:03 A.M. this was declared a high hazard day and extra engine companies were moved into the hilly area of the eastern part of the vast city to reinforce the companies stationed there. The humidity was down to 9 percent and the wind was twenty-nine miles per hour.

The engine companies sent to the eastern suburbs did not have long to wait for action. At 8:10 A.M. a fire started in a dump. Note the sequence of alarms.

8:15 A.M. first alarm—four engines
8:18 A.M. second alarm—four engines
8:20 A.M. third alarm—two engines
8:22 A.M. fourth alarm—three engines
8:26 A.M. fifth alarm

By this time headquarters realized they had a situation of

the utmost seriousness and sent fifteen more engine companies and two air tankers.

The first-alarm companies had a one-acre brush fire, but they never came anywhere near getting ahead of it. Driven by the Santa Ana wind, the flames roared through the chaparral brush. Clouds of burning embers swirled upward and were whipped to leeward by the strong wind to settle by the hundreds on the wooden shingles of expensive homes.

This type of fire jumps. The firemen never know where the next roof fire will be; next door to a burning dwelling or a half mile away. Moreover, a blazing shingle roof creates more brands and sparks than any other sort of fire. Every shingle roof that caught sent up red-hot embers by the hundreds.

The fire roared through the brush to within ten feet of some of the houses, setting the walls on fire by radiated heat and cracking the window glass so that it dropped out and permitted the fire to enter the interior. The houses built on stilts on the steep slopes were easy victims when the chaparral brush under them began to burn. Sometimes fire attacked the roof and underneath at the same time and the building was soon hopelessly involved.

By 10:35 A.M. fifty-nine pieces of apparatus were at work. By 12:30 P.M. ninety-six fire engines were on the scene and well they might be, for this had become a conflagration of the first magnitude. Finally, when county and out-of-town apparatus reached the scene, 154 fire engines were at work, and fifty-four other vehicles were doing various auxiliary duties. Fourteen air tankers were in action and they dropped 266,-200 gallons of slurry on the flames.

The pilots of the planes dropping slurry on the fire proved

extremely valuable as scouts, using their radios to send information to field headquarters of any ground developments they observed. Shortly after 4:00 P.M. one pilot reported burning shingles landing in Mandeville Canyon, a residential district not previously threatened. By this time twenty-five Civilian Defense outfits, a number of forestry units, and thirty-five out-of-town companies, responding according to mutual-aid plans, were on the fire scene. With the Los Angeles fire apparatus already mentioned and fourteen air tankers dropping fire-retardant liquids, a truly enormous assemblage of fire-fighting forces was at work.

Therefore, when the plane pilot's message arrived, it was possible to dispatch fifty fire engines to the Mandeville Canyon suburb within a couple of hours. They made a massive attack on the fire at this point and stopped it cold. From this time on, control of the fire was gradually established, and by four o'clock next morning it could be stated officially that it was in hand.

Los Angeles, in its outer east-suburban reaches, had suffered grievously. Destroyed were 505 buildings, mostly homes, and sixty-four others were damaged. The loss was over $24,000,000. So much for this expensive lesson in what a forest fire can do and the folly of permitting roofs made of wooden shingles. The fire-fighting was excellent, the number of fire engines tremendous. Yet no fire department in the world can stop a fire that travels overhead by way of burning wood fragments that fall as much as two miles away on bone-dry wooden shingles. The firemen never knew where the next roof fire would break out. A veritable army of firemen and volunteers were on the scene, but, even so, there was not enough manpower.

And here is a lesson in how intelligent people fail to think ahead. We enumerate the examples in this properous and enlightened community.

1. Wooden shingle roofs were widely used even though the records of nearly a hundred years' experience show that nothing is more likely to permit a fire to spread than wooden shingles. The painful experiences of dozens of cities were ignored by these people.

2. Although many homes had swimming pools containing up to 50,000 gallons of water, few owners had provided any way a fire engine could reach the pool to draft water. Fences and hedges obstructed access. No driveway or path provided a way a fire engine could reach the pool.

3. Home owners who love the picturesque built houses on steep slopes, supporting the downhill side on wooden uprights or stilts. Chaparral brush came close, so when it burned the intense heat rose under the house and ignited it. Many people never think a fire can occur on their property, because one never has occurred. So they did not worry about the chaparral brush.

4. This same type of thinking explains why so many home owners permitted brush to grow close to their houses. Probably it seemed romantic and close to nature. But nature can be a tough customer, as they learned when the fire roared through the brush, ignited the walls of the houses and the eaves, cracked the windows, and entered the interiors. Even a fire-resistive roof cannot save a house in this situation.

Another demonstration was to come, this one of the value of forests to man and the unhappy results when the forest is destroyed. Even a forest of brush, of no value as saw timber, can nevertheless be of great value to man. This the local people had learned by previous unhappy experience and they needed no further demonstration, but they got it, nonetheless.

As soon as the fire was under control, the flood-control officials, fully realizing the danger of six thousand acres from which all vegetation had been burned, began delivering sand bags and sand so residents could make dikes to protect their properties from inundation. Rye grass seed was distributed by the truck load in the hope that the local people would get it planted on the slopes and that it would sprout and grow a little and check the run off when a substantial rainfall occurred. Any growing thing is some help in slowing the run-off of a heavy rainfall. These hillsides had been absolutely denuded by the heat of the furious brushfire.

The efforts of the flood-control authorities were unavailing, for twelve days later a hard rain that totaled 1.88 inches hit the area and other heavy rains came in the weeks following. Vast amounts of mud flowed into many of the expensive homes in these suburban districts, causing heavy damage to houses that had escaped the fire. Of this harsh visitation of nature it could at least be said that it was not as bad as the fire and the residents philosophically turned to the task of shoveling and washing and restoring the parts of their structures weakened by the surging flood waters.

There are some things that can be done to reduce the destruction caused by forest fires which every year blacken areas of the woodland that makes our country beautiful, ruin trees that could become saw timber for our lumber industry, and often overwhelm summer camps, country barns, and dwellings and occasionally become a conflagration as in Los Angeles and Berkeley. Such fires can occur anywhere. For example, on a sunny, windy April day in 1941 a big grass fire assaulted the town of Marshfield, Massachusetts, and the conflagration, consuming 450 buildings, was not checked until it burned down to the shore of the Atlantic Ocean.

Every individual can help. To begin with, he can heed the requests of Smokey the Bear, that well-known friend of our forests and wild life. Always crush a cigarette dead out, says Smokey. Do not flip it into the grass or the bushes. Be sure the camp fire is out, if you are cooking in the woods. Drench the fire with water or cover it with wet earth.

Do not set fire to dry grass in the spring so you may see green grass a few days sooner. Choose a damp day to burn brush or rubbish. Never leave a fire unattended. Have a shovel, a pail of water, or a tank pump on hand.

If you own woodland, make a fire lane or more than one with an area of bare dirt. A fire lane grown over with grass or weeds is no use, the flames will race through such a spot on a dry day in spring.

If you are in or near woodland, keep an eye out for persons, particularly boys, who may have the notion that a fire is interesting. Incendiarism is the cause of an important percentage of forest fires. If you see even a small fire, go to the nearest fire-alarm box and pull the hook. Or put in a telephone call to the fire department. Never be fearful of bothering firemen with a small fire. The time to hit a fire is when it is small.

Do not be afraid of sounding a needless alarm. The firemen are paid to investigate even the suspicion of a fire. Fire apparatus standing in the station while a fire is developing is doing no good whatsoever. So if you see smoke, get the apparatus rolling. Many a fire has become serious because those who could have sent in the alarm have hesitated or been timid.

It may be useful here to dispose of the idea advanced by some not very intelligent person that every response to a fire alarm costs the city or town fifty dollars. Probably the chap who thought this one up took the annual cost of maintaining the fire department, divided it by the number of fire alarms in the year, and came out with the fifty-dollar figure. To follow this logic, it is obvious that if in a fortunate year the number of fire alarms was but half as many, then the cost of responding to each alarm would be one hundred dollars. And were it a bad year, with plenty of false alarms pulled by miscreants, and the number of responses doubled, the cost of answering an alarm would be not fifty, but twenty-five dollars.

In all of the above instances the cost of the fire department, mostly payroll, would be the same number of dollars. We have taken space to dispose of this notion because it appears to be widespread and it is dangerous thinking. It may cause the average man to hesitate and possibly not pull the box at a time when he has good reason to suspect that a fire has started.

Let it be stated flatly that the only cost of a fire-department response to an alarm is the amount of gasoline used to take the apparatus to the box. Fire engines rarely wear out. Instead, they deteriorate over the years, usually twenty or more, or they become obsolete. The tires do not wear out. They are replaced because they are old.

One other thing the average citizen can do to help in a forest fire. In such a situation the great need is manpower. Everyone who can use a broom or a shovel, carry a can of water, or put on a pack pump is valuable. It is not a time when experts are needed. Every shovelful of dirt counts. Do not overexert. Take it slow and easy, as the experienced ones do. If you are under the doctor's orders, watch the fire. If you are not, get in there and fight.

17

Modern Fire-fighting Equipment

OVER A CENTURY has passed since the early models of the steam fire engine replaced the hand tubs and their enormous crews of enthusiastic and sometimes turbulent volunteers. The steam fire engine gradually developed from a crude and cumbersome machine to a powerful, easily handled, and really beautiful piece of apparatus. It was the mainstay of American fire departments over the years until the time when mechanical engineering succeeded in harnessing the gasoline motor to the task of driving a fire engine to the fire and the additional task of running the pump upon arrival at the fire.

The era of the steam fire engine was a glorious time in the history of fire fighting. There was romance in the hand tubs, drawn by fifty men and in their fierce pumping rivalries at the fire. Romance of another sort the steamer had, with its two- or three-horse hitch galloping down the street, smoke trailing from the stack, the driver, whip in hand, urging his team to greater speed and the hose wagon, loaded with men, going on ahead to lay its lines if it were a working fire. The ladder truck and the chemical were with the steamer and the hose wagon and the chief and his one-horse buggy completed the group.

From all directions came call men to answer the alarm, leaving their jobs at the sound of the bells and whistles that counted out the alarm for all to hear. Some of the call men managed to hop on the rear step of the hose wagon or the running board of the ladder truck. Some ran, some were on bicycles. In this crowd streaming toward the fire were boys of all ages and those men called sparks or buffs who were never so busy they could not manage to be on hand if there was something burning.

When it was pumping, the steamer was at its finest. Smoke, driven by the exhaust steam from the cylinders, stabbed upward in a straight column as high as the third story of a house. She rocked up and down on her springs with the driving thrust of her pistons. The fly wheel was a blur of motion, the stoker was busy tossing cannel coal into the firebox, red embers flecked the black smoke column, the engineer with his long-snouted oil can walked around his machine, attending to his oil cups.

From the hydrant the big black suction hose ran to the steamer's intake and from the outlet gates ran two, three, and very occasionally four lines of hose to the burning building or to a deck gun or water tower in the street in front of the fire. The steady beat from the cylinders, the motion, the stiff hose lines, the towering smoke columns, the flashing pistons;

all told the story of the power and the glory of steam in action.

In the days of the hand tub, in the days of the steamer, it was the pump that was the backbone of the fire department. Water is what puts out fires and the two-fisted champion of the fire department that slugs it out with the enemy was and is now the pump. Today it is a pump driven by a gasoline motor instead of human muscle or steam. The ladder company is also part of the backbone of a department of any size. Their first task is to rescue those in the burning building. After that they ladder the building and open it up so the men with the water lines can get to the seat of the fire and hit it.

The pumper or engine company of today comes near to being a complete fire department in one vehicle. It has a pump with a capacity of five hundred gallons per minute on the smaller sizes; in city work the standard capacity is 750 or a thousand gallons per minute. Some cities have pumps with a capacity as high as 1500 gallons per minute. The pump is under the seat, if it is a rotary or centrifugal, and if it is a piston pump it is mounted on the very front, ahead of the motor. The piston pump is rare today, although many consider it the finest ever made. It takes more room on the vehicle and because it is more complex, it requires an excellent mechanic to maintain it.

The engine carries its own hose in a capacious body behind the driver's seat. A water tank with two hundred or more gallons and a reel of "'chemical" hose will take care of a small fire. Sometimes one-and-a-half-inch hose is used in pumping from this tank, often termed the "booster" tank, and a "big" line (two and a half inches) is run to the hydrant so that there will be water when the tank is empty. A good one-and-a-half-inch line will take care of a smart fire and it can be put into action from the booster tank very swiftly. Speed counts heavily.

On the engine are two or three short ladders, one of them usually an extension type capable of reaching a third-floor window. Often a "gun" is carried, a large-stream appliance or "deluge" set which will receive three big lines and deliver one massive stream that will make an impression on a really bad fire. This gun will receive all of the pumping capacity of a first-class pumping engine and deliver it in the large stream that is necessary to cope with a dangerous fire threatening to spread to other buildings.

The engine carries tools, such as axes, jimmies, and plaster hooks for inside work. It is often necessary to tear away part of a structure to get at a fire. Compartments contain first-aid equipment, oxygen masks, lights, and often an inhalator for emergency resuscitation procedures. Thus it is that if no other apparatus appears or if this is the only engine in town, the pump can do every operation that is required.

With the ladder truck, which appears in a fire department if it is at all beyond the stage of a small town, we find specialization. The pump is the fundamental piece that can do everything; the ladder truck does only certain things. And does them better. Here are ladders of all sizes; a long one of forty feet to take care of a fourth-story window or the roof of a sizable building, short ones to enter a cellar by way of a trap door, roof ladders with hooks on them to put over the ridge-pole of a pitched-roof house so the men can chop holes and get at an attic fire. And all lengths in between.

The so-called city service truck has no aerial ladder. It is for small towns where there are no buildings of any considerable height. All larger communities have one or more aerial-ladder trucks, and some smaller places are deciding that they should have one. The advantage of an aerial ladder is very great. This is a long ladder of the extension type which is raised by mechanical means and is usually seventy-five or eighty-five feet in length, although some are one hundred feet long.

If the truck pulls up in front of a burning building where people are at the upper windows shouting for help, the tiller man snatches off the big wheel with which he steers the rear wheels and climbs to the ground. The driver jumps to the levers that operate the aerial and the "big stick" begins to rise. Another lever operates the turntable on which this ladder is based; it turns until it is even with the window at which a man trapped by fire behind him is standing. Then the driver works the elevating lever so that the aerial ladder eases down toward the window sill. If this job is well done the tip of the ladder comes to rest so that it is a foot and a half above the window sill and the man waiting at the window for rescue can seize the side of the ladder for support and get out onto the top rung.

Usually one of the ladder crew has gone up the ladder while it is getting into position, so he is there to help the person out of the window and onto one of the top rungs. This can save a possible misstep and a fall. This assistance from a fireman is particularly important if the person being rescued is infirm or is a woman or a child.

If there are people at other windows awaiting rescue, the operator starts to move the ladder on its turntable while the first person is still coming down. There is not a second to waste when a ladder truck pulls up in front of a large tenement, lodging house, or hotel that is seriously involved. The aerial ladder does all this with one man at the controls, for it is power operated. To raise one of the truck's forty-foot ladders requires four, or better still, six men to get it into place. The aerial has length and can rescue a person from an eighth-floor window.

The ladder truck is the fundamental rescue unit, even though today in large cities we have rescue wagons with special equipment, such as electric saws, acetylene cutting torches, and oxygen sets for people suddenly stricken by smoke. The ladder truck has a wide assortment of tools. Every fire engine has an ax, a jimmie, and a plaster hook. In addition to these the ladder truck has shovels and brooms for removing debris from a building after the fire is out and an assortment of wrenches, tin cutters, hammers, and saws for dealing with situations inside a building.

Ladder trucks carry a battering ram. Six men can seize the ram by the handles and slug a breach in a brick wall. The ladder truck's cellar pipe, with a two-and-a-half-inch line connected to it, can be thrust through a hole in a floor to deliver a spray in all directions. They can be used in a cellar so choked with smoke that no one can enter by the stairway. Quite well known is the landing net, usually folded as a half circle and carried on the side of the apparatus. This is used as a last resort in situations where so many occupants await rescue that some threaten to jump before the ladder gets to them. This can be understood if the fire is so fierce that the person's back is being singed. It takes a large crew to hold a landing net. Most of the firemen are busy with the ladders, so a landing net is often manned by policemen and bystanders. It works if the one who jumps manages to land in the center of the net and if he does not leap from too high a story. If his drop is too great his velocity is such that the net sags and he strikes the ground. Then he is likely to be a multiple fracture case or dead on arrival at the hospital.

Another feature of rescue work is common with ladder companies located near a pond or river. In the fire station they have a small boat which can be attached to the tip of the aerial ladder when they get a "pond call" for a person who has fallen through thin ice in winter or who has been tipped from his canoe in summer. Sometimes the rescue company or one of the engine companies has a boat carried on a pair of automobile wheels for responses to a pond call.

For the purpose of water rescue the ladder company also has a shotgun with a plug to which is attached a heaving line about the size of fish line. They fire the gun and the plug shoots out toward the person in the water, with the heaving line snaking after it. If the person in the water pulls in this light line, there will be a substantial rope attached to it. Then he can put his arms in the loop of the rope and the firemen will haul him ashore. Afterward he gets a fast ride to the hospital in the police ambulance, with sirens, and is given the immersion treatment when he arrives.

If it is a case of one who has fallen through thin ice, the firemen often lay ladders on the ice to spread the weight of the fireman who crawls out to snatch the victim from the water. Using a ladder in this way a man can proceed safely over ice so thin that it would break after two steps if he attempted to walk across it. Some park departments having charge of ponds place a ladder on a rack on the shore at various points where people are likely to go skating in the winter. Many people have poor judgment as to the strength of ice and it is a foregone conclusion that a number of skaters will fetch up in the water every winter. For the average person who happens to see someone go into the water there is one excellent unvarying rule. Get to the nearest fire-alarm box, pull the hook, and remain there until the apparatus arrives so that you may direct them to the scene of the accident. Or get to a telephone and put in the pond call, always being sure to state the exact location of the accident. Exceptions: unless it is summer and you have a life-saving certificate or there is a rowboat handy. Even then, it is better to ask some one to pull the box or telephone so help may be on the way while you are making the rescue attempt.

On the tip of every aerial ladder is affixed a nozzle to which leads a line of hose. At the base of the ladder there is connected to this hose a Y or Siamese, so that two lines can be run into it. This makes the aerial ladder a water tower when two strong engine lines are hooked up to the Siamese. From the nozzle at the tip a good stream can be delivered at the eighth- or ninth-floor level. We saw a fire involving the entire top floor of a seven-story apartment house handled this way. Six aerial ladders using the nozzles at their tips plus a deluge set on the flat roof of a three-story building next door knocked the fire down. This fire originated on the top floor, and the building later required only a new top story.

These, the engine (pumper) and the ladder truck, are most of the fire-fighting force. There are some less common pieces of apparatus that deserve a few lines. One is a new type of ladder truck called a "snorkel," first used for important work by the Chicago fire department. It does the work, yet has no ladders. The snorkel has three or four arms joined together and operated by power. These lie folded on the bed of the truck and when operated, they unfold and extend and on the end is an enormous bucket large enough to hold two or three men.

In rescue work the fireman in the bucket can be raised to the window where someone is waiting. He can grasp the victim and get him into the bucket, where he is much safer than climbing down the rungs of an aerial ladder. He can be lowered quickly to the ground, where he will at once be snatched from the bucket. Then the operator raises the giant levers so the fireman in the bucket will be at another window to make a rescue.

In Chicago, where nine of the snorkel trucks are in service, they played an important part in removing passengers from the elevated railway structure after a wreck. Some of the injured were brought down from the elevated on stretchers laid across the basket of the snorkel. This type of apparatus is being acquired by a considerable number of cities.

Another piece of apparatus rarely seen is the quadruple combination, a city-service ladder truck with a pump, a hose body, a full complement of ladders, and a booster water tank for small fires. This attempt at an entire fire department in one truck seems to have gone too far and few of them were ever put in service. Often a ladder truck and a pump must work at different points at the fire scene. To have them all on one truck is likely to diminish the usefulness of either one or the other feature of the truck. However, it should be noted that many ladder trucks today have booster tanks containing from one hundred to two hundred gallons of water. This small water line is very useful in chasing a fire through the partitions of a house or in extinguishing a roof fire caused by burning brands. Both of these tasks fall frequently to the laddermen.

Large cities have protective or salvage companies, sometimes financed by the insurance interests. Water pouring down from a fire in a story above can be very distructive in warehouse and factory situations. The protective or salvage men spread rubber covers over merchandise, move what they can out of the building, and see to drainage of water from the floors by way of gutters and pipes installed for that purpose in many modern structures. Their work is very important when something has activated the sprinklers needlessly. They have squeegees and mops and brooms for this work. So, too, do the ladder companies, for salvage is one of their many duties.

In Detroit the department has what they term a boat tender. It is a fine hose wagon with two deck guns and a body with a full suit of hose. In the St. Clair River the department has a fireboat capable of delivering 16,000 gallons per minute. The boat tender responds to every alarm to which the fireboat responds. It takes three-inch lines from the fireboat's outlets, runs them to its deck guns, and hits the fire from the landward side with two streams of massive power.

If the fire is not on the river front, but within two blocks, the fireboat couples to headers, which are mains running two blocks inland and provided with hydrants. From these the boat tender takes lines which may be connected to one or both of its deck guns or may be used as hand lines, as the need may be. By using this boat tender in these various situations extra value is obtained from the truly tremendous capability of the fireboat's pumps.

When any waterfront structure or ship is burning, one or

more fireboats are of tremendous value. They have enormous pumping capability, an unlimited water supply, and a position which could not possibly be reached by any land fire apparatus. They are truly the heavy artillery of the fire department of any port city, whether situated on salt water, a lake, or a river. Their monitor nozzles, one of which is on the boat's short mast, deliver streams of massive volume and power.

We recall a masterful use of the fireboat's power in a very delicate situation. A large coal wharf was fully involved, and the streams of the fireboats, tearing through the wooden structures, had knocked down the flames everywhere except in the big derrick, which still blazed fiercely. If the wooden derrick was allowed to burn out, it might give way in a place that would sent it crashing through the roof of a nearby storage shed as yet untouched by the fire and stacked with valuable merchandise.

The streams of the big monitor nozzles of one of the fireboats, with their great power and pressure and volume, could easily extinguish the burning wooden derrick tower. Yet the chief's problem was that the pressure from a fireboat's stream would probably knock the weakened derrick tower over and it would most certainly plunge through the roof of the unburned storage shed. That problem he solved with an order to direct a heavy stream a few feet to windward of the burning derrick. The wind was gentle, yet sufficient to carry spray from the big stream onto the burning tower in about the volume a heavy thunder shower would produce.

Fifteen minutes of this treatment was enough to extinguish the fire in the derrick tower, and there it stood, awaiting the time when it would be removed carefully by a wrecking crew.

A fireboat, big and powerful, has its limitations, mostly due to its size. It cannot be used in odd corners or narrow places. Particularly requiring some strong streams of water is the underside of a burning wharf, a location completely out of the reach of streams from a fireboat. For such situations some departments have "pup" fireboats, motor craft thirty feet in length capable of working in close quarters.

These "pups" are of shallow draft, enabling them to get close at low tide or in shallow streams or reaches. Instead of a propellor, which can foul on floating objects or ground in shallow places, their motive power is a pair of water-jet streams at the stern that give them excellent speed and maneuverability.

For such "little fellows" these boats can deal ferocious blows at any fire on or near the water. Delivering 3500 to 7000 gallons per minute from monitor nozzles mounted bow and stern, these boats are equal to at least two regular land companies at a fire in a marina, or on piers or wharves or in any building near enough to the water to be within the long reach of the stream from the monitor or deck gun. From connections aboard, good lines may be taken to any fire ashore.

As a rescue company these craft are superb. They can proceed at speed to any small craft in trouble and pick personnel out of the water or off the keel of a capsized sailboat. And if necessary, they can deliver the first important blow at any burning motorboat or at a fire aboard a ship of any size.

Not to be forgotten in any fight along the shore or aboard ship is the power of the monitor nozzles mounted on tugboats and Coast Guard and Navy vessels. Installation of fire-fighting equipment aboard such vessels is no great problem, for the power plant and the source of water is already there. To provide a pump, some piping and one or more properly placed monitor nozzles add one more protective unit to that particular port area. And in a really bad waterfront fire there can never be too many streams.

The problem of oil and gasoline fires is in better control than one would suppose, considering their extreme flammability. Since every one knows the danger that lies in these liquids, extrordinary precautions are taken to control them. Almost universally an oil tank is surrounded by dikes or low cement walls capable of confining its contents if it ruptures. Thus if it burns and bursts, the blazing contents remain within the dikes and burn out. Were it not for the dikes, the burning oil would flow in various directions and set nearby oil tanks on fire. As it is, the fire is usually confined to one tank.

Lightning is the most important cause of fires in oil tanks. Care is taken to install proper lightning rods to conduct the electricity into the ground. Hatches and covers are kept tightly sealed so vapors will not escape. Vents are provided for the relief of internal pressures.

Large oil refineries and tank farms not only take all possible measures to localize any fire, as with dikes and strategically located shut-off valves, but they also have their own fire-fighting forces well provided with foam equipment and fog nozzles. Such installations are rarely in a settled community. It is when oil and gasoline are in smaller lots around town that a municipal fire department has a real problem.

When a large tank truck proceeding down a principal street is in a collision, the steel plates sometimes rupture and gasoline pours onto the pavement. If it is ignited by a spark, the local fire department is in for a time of it. Most needed is foam powder. A line is connected to a foam generator, a hopper-like device, into which the foam powder is slowly poured. Another line runs from the foam generator to the fire and a stream like shaving lather arches onto the burning gasoline, forming a thick layer of suds on top of the blazing liquid. This shuts off the oxygen supply and the fire is out in a remarkably short time.

That is the result if the burning area is not too large. In a more serious fire, fog nozzles play a water mist onto the flames, which both cuts off oxygen and cools the burning materials. The fronts of buildings in danger of being ignited by radiated heat are protected by fog streams and by regular engine lines. Both serve to keep the structures cool enough so that they will not catch fire.

Water is used carefully, either as fog or as solid streams, to protect buildings against radiated heat. Oil is lighter than water and will float upon it, still burning. In the past, embarrassing situations have arisen from the use of powerful water streams on an oil fire. The water flows down the street, the burning oil or gasoline floating on it.

In one such instance the water and blazing gasoline poured down the gutter and into a catch basin that drained into a brook. Down the brook went this blazing stream for a quarter mile and set fire to a house with a veranda that came to the edge of the water. The veranda was undoubtedly a pleasant place on a hot summer evening and the man who built it never foresaw danger from such a fire. Before the fire department could get to this one, the house was heavily damaged.

To run out of foam powder at a fire like this is of the

utmost seriousness. It has happened a few times and in some areas a central depot of foam has been established to take care of part of the county. A hurry call brings an additional supply of foam powder.

At airports the crash truck is always ready to deliver substantial quantities of foam. The Portland, Oregon, airport had a situation where two aircraft collided upon landing and both burst into flames.

One of them, a military plane, was upside down with the pilot hanging in his harness. The crash truck raced across the airfield and instantly directed its stream of foam upon the blazing aircraft. The plane was covered with a thick layer of lather that made it look as if a gargantuan barber had been at work with his brush and shaving mug. The fire was snuffed out and the pilot removed with only minor injuries.

In aviation, fire is most dreaded. Inventive genius may some day be able to design an airplane in which the fire danger is less than it is today. To do so is a pressing problem. Until that time the crash trucks and the foam technique are the only worthwhile counter-measure and they are used whenever they offer hope.

The foam technique is used when an incoming plane radios the airport that is is having trouble with its landing gear. That means a crash landing, and, of course, the danger that the plane will burst into flames when it comes down on its belly. At once the control tower tells the plane which runway to land on and the crash trucks are ordered to that runway to cover the ground with foam. Then they stand by as the plane comes in, ready to let drive with streams of foam at the first suspicion of fire.

Using foam on oil fires is standard operating procedure. A

new type of foam, much lighter, is valuable in fighting oil fires and has other and unusual uses. This foam, when introduced into a stream of water, expands to a volume one thousand times greater than the stream which carries it.

A chief can use this to attack a fire in a place into which he is reluctant to send his men, such as a room where there may be lethal gases or a weak floor. The foam will fill a room to the ceiling, oxygen is excluded, and the fire goes out. Gradually the foam subsides and disappears. Thus a fire in a dangerous place is extinguished without risk to the lives of the firemen.

An example of the value of such an extinguishing agent is a fire that occurred twenty years ago in the basement of a big city fur store. The first company in took an engine line down the stairway to tackle a brisk blaze on the far side of the place. The smoke thickened and the officer at the head of the stairs found he had lost touch with his men below.

There was no response to his shouts. A rescue squad with masks of the type that have a small oxygen tank connected were sent down after the men. They got them; three dead and one so badly affected he later was retired from the fire service.

The basement had no openings to the outside and the fire had used up all the oxygen. Men could not live in such an atmosphere. This situation of exhausted oxygen is not uncommon. Now, with the new foam, if there appears to be any such possibility, or if deadly gases may be present, the officer in command need take no risks. An order to fill the basement with foam will settle the matter and it all can be done by a man standing at the head of the stairs with a foam line.

The rescue company's vehicle and lighting truck are important fire-department auxiliaries and present no unusual features of design or function. In an actual rescue operation the rescue company and a ladder company always respond together. If some citizen is in difficulty in a hard-to-reach place, there is nothing like having a good selection of ladders right at hand.

A rescue company is often called on to do first-aid work. It is easy to step to the telephone and call the fire department. The response is instantaneous. To get a doctor might take half or three quarters of an hour. If it is a bad bleeding case, these men can stop it sufficiently so the victim can safely be taken to the hospital. If it is a heart attack, the rescue squad has an oxygen tank and a face mask. One of the crew rides in the ambulance to the hospital with the victim, seeing to it that the oxygen set is working properly at all times. Many lives have been saved by their speedy action. They have a practical knowledge of what to do in emergency medical situations, and their arrival inspires confidence in the victim and the family. Particularly after a boating, swimming, or skating mishap is their first-aid technique valuable.

In small towns one finds some interesting fire apparatus, often of local design to meet situations frequent in that community. A water system and hydrants are much more common today in the smaller places, yet there are many buildings far beyond the reach of public water. And there are large tracts of brush and forest land. Thus we find the smaller towns have fire apparatus carrying large quantities of water with them.

A forest-fire truck is always found in a town fire station. It carries a water tank of from three to five hundred gallons with a reel of three quarter-inch hose. A dozen pack pumps or Indian cans are aboard; also a portable pump that can draft from a well, a brook, a pond, or a hole dug in a swamp. This truck, well manned, can strike a strong blow at a fire in its early stages.

Another design is a jeep with a two hundred-gallon water tank and a small pump with its own motor. This piece with its four wheel drive can go through the brush to the fire line and then move across the face of the fire delivering a strong water stream directly into the flames. Since the pump has its own motor, it can operate even while the jeep is in motion.

One town managed to acquire an Army half-track, in which they installed a large water tank and a pump driven by its own motor. Forest fires were unusually troublesome in this community and one of the principal problems was getting into difficult and remote brush areas with their fire apparatus. The half-track, with the greater power and capability of a tracked vehicle, is able to go through the meanest bramble patches, over stone walls, and across soggy stretches that would mire a wheeled vehicle. With the blows it delivers at brush fires, many of the town's problems are solved.

Useful, too, are old oil trucks loaded with water and carrying a small motor to drive the pump. Forest fires are the principal problem, but if two or more such pieces of apparatus tackle a fire in a house well beyond the area of hydrants, they often hold the fire until the regular pumping engines, perhaps with the help of out-of-town apparatus, can lay a long line, with one engine relaying the water to another. That gives them an engine line of two-and-a-half-inch hose and such a line is the king of all fire fighting equipment. It is usually enough to knock down a house fire, with the smaller streams to help.

A method that enables the tank vehicles to keep continuous streams on the fire is to have one of them pump its water into one of the others that is playing on the fire and then race down the road to a hydrant to refill its tank. With one acting as a supply unit for the others, it is possible to keep streams of water on the fire. If all of them turned their streams on the fire, then when they were all empty, unless the fire was completely extinguished, the flames would quickly increase and they would surely lose the building. These tank fire engines sometimes get help from householders and volunteers who carry water to them, as did the old-time bucket brigades.

Not from a small town, but from New York City we learn of one of the newest and most unusual pieces of fire apparatus. This is a pump of tremendous power and capability, called the Superpumper. It has a capacity of over 8000 gallons a minute. It develops very high pressure and requires special hose four and a half inches in diameter. With it operate one or more hose wagons or tenders with the special large-diameter hose required.

The Superpumper has been operating in New York long enough so that actual examples of its tremendous capability are at hand. The hose wagons that run with it carry large deck guns or monitors called water cannon. Taking one or more four-and-a-half-inch lines from the Superpumper, they throw a stream with a five-hundred-foot reach.

One of its victories was a fire in which a row of twelve three-story tenement houses, three deckers, was heavily involved. As usual in this type of building the rear piazzas were a roaring inferno. Behind this row of buildings was a narrow alley and then another row of a dozen three deckers facing another street.

The fire was quite out of hand. It appeared possible that here was the start of a conflagration that might involve an entire area of New York. Along with a number of extra alarms went out the special call for the Superpumper. When it arrived, it took a position on the next street. One of its hose wagons was placed in front of the row of three deckers not yet involved. One of the big four-and-a-half-inch lines was run from the Superpumper to the hose wagon or tender.

From the water cannon or deck gun on the hose wagon came a stream of such reach that it arched completely over the row of uninvolved tenement houses to strike squarely the roaring fire in the rear piazzas of the three deckers that were burning. The men operating the water cannon did not see their target; they regulated the elevation and the traverse of their stream in obedience to the hand signals of a man on the roof of the building opposite their position.

Burned fragments of boards and debris of every sort flew about, windows crashed in, and blazing areas were blackened as the mighty stream moved back and forth along the rear of the blazing buildings. The stream had volume and it had pressure; the blows it struck were decisive and the danger that the fire might communicate from one row of structures to the other vanished. What remained was an ordinary job for engine crews with hand lines and ladder men with axes and plaster hooks working in the interiors.

Another Superpumper job was a fire in a five-story ice house with blank walls; the last building on a dead-end street with poor water supply. The interior of an ice house with hay and bark and sawdust for insulation and wooden floors and partitions and ice slides has the makings of a furious fire, as any one who lives in the northern part of the United States well knows.

A four-and-a-half-inch line from the Superpumper was laid down this dead-end street, and from it, by a specially made connection, six lines were taken. Three were used to supply a deluge set and the others were used as hand lines. The fire was surrounded, confined, and then extinguished.

Another one of the Superpumper's fires occurred in an old theater, two hundred by two hundred feet, which had been converted into a candy factory. This old building with an ordinary wooden interior well dried out by the passage of years, its contents inflammable, was well involved when the first-alarm apparatus arrived. A special call for the Superpumper was sent.

One of the tenders or hose wagons was spotted in front of the building. On its water cannon or deck gun a four-inch tip was used and lines were laid from the Superpumper. This gigantic stream swept entirely through the building, the torrent of water carrying with it an odd assortment of caramels, bon-bons, and candy boxes. What had been a fire with possibilities of spreading to other structures was knocked down with great swiftness. Crews with hand lines finished the job.

Brooklynites had a preview of the Superpumper's capabilities when, on August 12, 1965, not long before the formal demonstration was to take place, a ten-million-dollar lumberyard fire occurred. The Superpumper was raced to the scene. All hands were anxious to see how it would perform under actual working conditions. And perform it did. Taking suction from the harbor, it ran all night long and delivered seven and a half million gallons of salt water to the fire.

New York at the time was suffering a serious water shortage. This use of salt water taken from the harbor by the Superpumper greatly reduced the drain on the city's reservoirs.

A few days later the new engine delivered another massive

blow to a multiple-alarm fire in a textile mill in Brooklyn. For those who witnessed these astounding exhibitions of the power and capability of the new machine, the formal demonstration a few days later was somewhat anticlimactic.

By reason of this engine's great capacity, it is a safety factor in the event that water mains are so injured by accident or explosion as to be out of service, as in the London blitz of 1940. Drafting from one of the rivers or the harbor, it can pump great distances through wide-diameter hose. From connections in the big hose, ordinary lines can be run to the fire. If the distance is so great as to result in significant loss of pressure, the lines taken from the big hose will be run to ordinary pumpers, which will boost the pressure and deliver the water to the fire scene. With this pump drafting through the special large hose, the city has an emergency water main. Such an arrangement would have been of incalculable value at the San Francisco fire, when most of the water mains were out of service because of earthquake shocks. It might be added, however, that engineering capability at that time was not equal to building such a pump, even if someone had conceived the idea.

The design and construction of the New York Superpumper, its hose, its tenders, its motor, its monitors (water cannon) was not easy. It required the very best capabilities of engineers in several fields and was very expensive. Yet, in the opinion of the New York Fire Department, it is worth what it cost. Another waterfront city ordering such a unit would be obliged to pay somewhat less, since development and design costs already have been paid.

Bibliography

Aitken, Frank W. and Hilton, Edward. *A History of the Earthquake and Fire in San Francisco.* San Francisco, Ed. Hilton Co., 1906.

Brayley, Arthur Wellington. *A Complete History of the Boston Fire Department, Including the Fire Alarm Service and the Protective Department From 1630 to 1888.* Boston, J. P. Dole & Co., 1889.

Bronson, William. *The Earth Shook, the Sky Burned.* New York, Doubleday, 1959.

Chandler and Company's Full Account of the Great Fire in Boston, 1872 (Pamphlet).

Coffin, Charles Carleton. *Story of the Great Fire: Boston Nov. 9-10, 1872 by Carleton, an Eye-witness.* Boston, Shepard and Gill, 1872.

Colonial Laws of Massachusetts Reprinted from Edition of 1672 with Supplements Through 1686. Published by Order of the City Council of Boston, 1887.

Conwell, Col. Russell H. *History of the Great Fire in Boston, Nov. 9 and 10, 1872.* Boston, B. B. Russell, 1873.

Cromie, Robert. *Great Chicago Fire.* New York, McGraw-Hill, 1958.

Dana, D. D. *The Fireman.* Boston, E. O. Libby, 1858.

Dougherty, Thomas F. and Kearney, Paul W. *Fire.* New York, G. P. Putnam's Sons, 1931.

BIBLIOGRAPHY

Hill, Charles T. *Fighting a Fire*. New York, Century, 1916.

Himmelwright, A. L. A. *San Francisco Earthquake and Fire*. New York, Roebling Construction Co., 1906.

Holzman, Robert S. *Romance of Firefighting*. New York, Harper & Bros., 1956.

Jones, Arthur B. *Salem Fire*. Boston, Gorham Press, 1914.

Keeler, Charles. *San Francisco Through Earthquake and Fire*. San Francisco, Paul Elder & Co., 1906.

Kennedy, John C. *Great Earthquake and Fire*. New York, Morrow, 1963.

Kenlon, John. *Fires and Fire-fighters: a History of Modern Fire-fighting with a Review of Its Development from Earliest Times*. New York, Geo. H. Doran Co., 1913.

Letters Written by a Gentleman in Boston to His Friend in Paris Describing the Great Fire with Introductory Chapter and Notes by Harold Murdock. Boston, Houghton, 1909.

Lewis, Lloyd and Smith, Henry Justin. *Chicago*. New York, Harcourt Brace, 1929.

Massachusetts Charitable Fire Society. *An Old Boston Institution; a Brief History. Organized 1792*. Boston, Little, 1893.

Miller and Others. *Fighting Fire: Great Fires of History*. Hartford, Dustin-Gilman, 1873.

Morris, John V. *Fires and Firefighters*. Boston, Little Brown, 1954.

Mutual Fire Insurance Companies. *Salem Conflagration and the Destruction of the Naumkeag Steam Cotton Co., June 25, 1914*. Boston, Author, 1914.

Pratt, William Merriam. *Burning of Chelsea*. Boston, Sampson Pub. Co., 1908.

Records Relating to the Early History of Boston Containing Miscellaneous Papers (Including the Great Fire of 1700). Boston, Municipal Printing Office, 1900.

Report of the Chicago Relief and Aid Society of Disbursements of Contributions for the Sufferers by the Chicago Fire. Cambridge, Riverside Press, 1874.

Report of the Commissioners Appointed to Investigate the Cause and Management of the Great Fire in Boston. Boston, Rockwell & Churchill, City Printers, 1873.

Searight, Frank T. *Doomed City*. Chicago, Laird & Lee, 1906.

Sewell, Alfred L. *The Great Calamity: Scenes, Incidents and Lessons of the Great Chicago Fire*. Chicago, Alfred L. Sewell, 1871.

BIBLIOGRAPHY

Sheldon, George W. *Story of the Volunteer Fire Department of the City of New York.* New York, Harper & Bros., 1882.

Williams, Harold A. *Baltimore Afire, Being an Account of One of America's Great Conflagrations.* Baltimore, Remington, 1954.

ALSO

Accounts in newspapers and magazines of the period, particularly

Harper's Weekly
Outlook
Overland
Current Literature
Scientific American
Review of Reviews

Publications of the National Fire Protection Association, including special fire reports on the Baltimore and the Fall River conflagrations.

Publications of the U.S. Forestry Service on forest fires and prevention.

Index

INDEX

INDEX

INDEX

INDEX